TV Astronomer

Thirty Years of
'The Sky at Night'

TV Astronomer

Thirty Years of 'The Sky at Night'

Patrick Moore

HARRAP

London

First published in Great Britain 1987
by HARRAP Ltd
19-23 Ludgate Hill, London EC4M 7PD

ISBN 0 245–54531–X

Designed by Roger Kohn

Phototypeset by Falcon Graphic Art Ltd
Wallington, Surrey

Printed and bound in Great Britain by
R. J. Acford Limited, Chichester, Sussex

◄(previous page) *Palomar
photograph of the Andromeda
Galaxy, M.31, which is just over
2,000,000 light-years away, and is
larger than our own Galaxy. It is a
spiral, but has been inconsiderately
placed almost edge-on to us.*

Contents

Foreword

Last year, 1986, BBC Television celebrated its first fifty years. For well over half that period a twenty-minute programme has been transmitted every four weeks; every single one in fact since April 1957 has been presented by one man — Patrick Moore. It is an extraordinary achievement, and as far as I can establish it is a world record. There have been many series that have had more episodes; there are programmes that have been running longer under different presenters – *Panorama*, for instance — but Patrick and *The Sky at Night* have returned to television screens up and down the country once every lunar month for the past thirty years.

Looking back at the records of 1957, one of the other highlights of the 'Talks Department' was a programme entitled *The Lost World of Kalahari*, 'a study on film of the desert pygmies'. So even then, with only fifty hours of television a week allowed by the Postmaster General, there was a varied diet for viewers. Incidentally, in the same BBC publication are the words 'The BBC's plans for the future include some form of transmission in colour'. The vagueness of that sentence seems remarkable to us, in 1987, as does the relatively unsophisticated state of astronomy in those days. We have now sent a spacecraft to meet a comet, the very idea of which would have been regarded as science fiction in 1957.

Patrick has entertained viewers of several generations with the fascinating development in astronomy. There are many highly respected astronomers who were encouraged to take up the subject as a profession through watching *The Sky at Night*. It must be the way Patrick tells it! Who else would connect a revolution in the Congo and the Royal Greenwich Observatory; a cheese-manufacturer and Uranus; a fried egg and our Milky Way; a Spanish taxi-driver and a solar eclipse; a boy's cricket team and the apparent position of the stars; and a dog walking uphill and the Moon? Confused? You won't be after reading this book. There are many more gems in here, and many tales — or should it be trails? — of disaster in the making of the programmes. Interwoven into all this, in Patrick's inimitable style, is the fascinating story of astronomy over the past thirty years. Anyway, enough from me. Cue Patrick!

Pieter Morpurgo
Producer, *The Sky at Night*

Preface

This book is in no way meant to be an autobiography, if only because nobody would be in the slightest degree interested. What I have tried to do is to tell the story of a programme, which has been running now for thirty years.

My thanks are due to many people: to the four 'long-term' producers, the late Paul Johnstone, Patricia Owtram, Patricia Wood and now Pieter Morpurgo; to Eric Ilett and Paul Michael Doherty for their models and computer illustrations; to Paul Bernard Doherty for his superb artwork; and of course to all those who have taken part in the programmes, as well as the directors and camera crews without whom no broadcasts of any sort would be possible. Finally, my thanks to the BBC itself. Broadcasting for so many years has been a great privilege; I hope that I have not let anybody down.

I am also most grateful to those who have helped in the production of this book. Paul Bernard Doherty has provided his usual magnificent illustrations; Barney D'Abbs has given me assistance in proof-reading. And I am, of course, deeply grateful to Pieter Morpurgo for his Foreword, and to the publishers, particularly Derek Johns and Roy Minton, for doing such a splendid job of production and putting the book through the press at breakneck speed!

PATRICK MOORE
Selsey, 1 February 1987.

1
At the Castle Gate

I had been in London, attending a meeting. The weather was typical of the spring of 1957 — cold, damp, even somewhat foggy — and the journey from Victoria to my nearest station, East Grinstead, was as awful as usual. British Rail had not yet coined the slogan 'This is the age of the train', but the average age of the trains on the East Grinstead line was, I think, about a hundred years, and the thirty-mile journey took a full two hours. Still, as I finally came indoors, there was an encouraging message waiting for me. 'You have been accepted for a television series. Please ring Paul Johnstone, at the BBC, as soon as possible.'

I was elated — after all, who wouldn't have been? I had never thought of myself as a television presenter, but I knew that the suggestion was going round the BBC, and early on the following morning I was on the telephone. Braving the railway once more — at that stage I hadn't a car; I couldn't afford one — I made my way to Lime Grove to talk things over.

The story had really begun some weeks earlier, with a programme about flying saucers. My lack of faith in space-crockery in general, and little green men from Mars in particu-lar, is complete; but Desmond Leslie, who was 'fronting' the pro-Saucer contingent, was an old friend of mine, and it was he who had suggested bringing me in as a thoroughly sceptical and reactionary astronomer. Paul Johnstone, who was a respectable scientist as well as a BBC producer, and who was therefore deeply involved in all such programmes, had been looking out for a presenter interested in astronomy, and evidently thought that I might be suitable. I had no degree; what should have been my Cambridge years, from 1940 to 1945, had been spent in the RAF, pottering about in various types of aircraft.[1] But Paul wanted someone who could talk, and this at least I could do.

We had a long discussion. What exactly was our aim? Could we manage a programme every month, slanted towards the total beginner and yet with enough solid material to entrap the well informed? Paul thought we could; so did I, even though at that stage my knowledge of television was virtually nil, and in any case television had nothing like the influence it has today. There was also the point that astronomy was still regarded as a somewhat eccentric study, practised by old men with long white beards who spent their working lives in lonely observatories 'looking at the stars', and possibly using crystal balls as well. We

---

[1] *I flew as a navigator, though at one stage I did take my pilot's wings. I remember that my Commanding Officer once watched me landing a Tiger Moth. In the evening, in the Mess, he gave me an old-fashioned look. 'Kid,' he said sadly, 'if you'd been a fighter pilot, you'd have won an Iron Cross!' I bought him a drink in a marked manner.*

◄ *The Lime Grove studio in 1958, when we were still using the enlarged planisphere as a 'prop'. We continued to do so until it disintegrated some years later.*

had a great many problems to face.

Since all this happened thirty years ago, I think I must say a little about the state of affairs at the time. The Space Age had not started; it was only in the following October that the Russians launched Sputnik 1, the first artificial satellite, which took many people by surprise and even caused considerable alarm in the West. (One man in Washington rang the Pentagon to say that a sputnik had landed in his garden and was now lodged in the top of a high tree; it proved to be a balloon, with 'upski' painted on the top and 'downski' on the bottom.) The great radio telescope at Jodrell Bank, in Cheshire, was barely in action, and was widely regarded by the general public as a waste of money. The idea of sending a man to the Moon was little more than a music-hall joke, except to those people who had taken the trouble to investigate; rockets were still classed solely with the V.2 weapons master-minded by Wernher von Braun. Generally speaking, anyone who could recognize the Plough and the Pole Star was doing rather well.

Television was, by 1987 standards, primitive. Of course it was all black-and-white; and because recordings were not up to standard, everything – so far as possible – was 'live', leaving a much greater scope for disaster than is usual today. There was little in the way of electronics, and producers were compelled to use all sorts of dodges, as I was to learn very soon in my BBC life.

One of the 'minor' problems was the selection of opening music, which is actually more important than might be thought. The usual suggestions, such as 'You Are My Lucky Star', were rejected out of hand. We also dismissed Holst's *Planets*, partly because it was too obvious and partly because it was astrological anyway. Finally we hit upon a movement from the

▲ *With my seventeenth-century orrery, which we used as an opening shot on the programme for many years.*

Sibelius suite *Pelléas et Mélisande*. It was called 'At the Castle Gate', and it proved to be a great success. We still use it, and have no thought of changing it. One temporary producer of the mid-1960s did want to replace it with something else; his head is still to be seen fixed to a plaque on my study wall.

We went to see Alfred Wurmser, a charming Viennese who lived in the Goldhawk Road; he had a dog named Till, who was about the size of a donkey but was nevertheless under the delusion that he was a lap-dog. Alfred made moving models out of cardboard, and he soon became enthusiastic, with the result that we continued to use the 'wurmsers' until Alfred decided to return to his native Austria. The original title of our programme was to be *Star Map*, but we soon changed this to *The Sky at Night*— just in time to make sure that the new title went into the *Radio Times*.

At that stage we had a stroke of luck. A bright comet appeared, and caused a great deal of popular interest. Could it be an omen?

► *Comet Arend-Roland; the picture shown on the very first* Sky at Night *programme in April 1957. The picture was taken by Eric Lindsay at Armagh, and shows the 'spike' beautifully. Alas, the comet will never return. I wish it well.*

Comets have often been classed as unlucky, and said to indicate various dire events in the near future, ranging from plagues to earthquakes, wars and even the end of the world. We knew better. A comet, after all, is a flimsy thing, made up of ices, thin gas and fine dust, so that it cannot hurt anyone; certainly no comet could knock the Earth out of its orbit — one might as well try to divert a charging hippopotamus by hurling a baked bean at it. The new comet, Arend-Roland (so named after the two Belgian astronomers who had discovered it), was unusual inasmuch as it appeared to have two tails, one pointing away from the Sun and the other towards it. Actually, the sunward 'tail' was due to nothing more than fine dust spread along the comet's path, but it looked intriguing, and for several evenings during April the comet was prominently visible with the naked eye. Frankly, it was much more imposing than Halley's Comet was to be almost three decades later.

Obviously, Arend-Roland had to be the main topic of our first programme. I took photographs of it, and managed to obtain others; we revised our original plans, even relegating an eclipse of the Moon to the last few minutes of the programme; and eventually we were ready for transmission — or so we hoped. Remember, I had been 'on the air' only once before, and I had no real idea of what to expect, particularly as I had no guest appearing on the programme with me.

Rehearsals seemed to go well. Even at that stage I had no word-for-word script; Paul trusted me to bring in the visuals (photographs, diagrams and general effects) at the right moments, and otherwise it was up to me. And at 10.30 on the evening of 26 April 1957 I was seated in my chair in the Lime Grove studio waiting for the red light over the television camera to come on.

Was I nervous? In a way, I suppose I was; I remember thinking 'My entire life depends upon what I do during the next fifteen minutes.' Then the screen on the monitor began to glow; I saw the words *The Sky at Night. A regular monthly programme presented by Patrick Moore*, and the series was launched. It did not then occur to me that I would still be broadcasting thirty years later.

2
Reaching for the Moon

I waited anxiously for reactions to that first programme. My thanks were due to the twin-tailed comet, and I was sorry to see it depart from our skies a few weeks later. It will never return — it had the misfortune to pass close to the giant planet Jupiter, and was unceremoniously hurled out of the Solar System altogether, so that even if *The Sky at Night* is still being broadcast a few tens of thousands of years hence my successor will be unable to welcome Arend-Roland back. Meanwhile, we all wanted to know whether we had made the programme (a) too elementary, (b) not elementary enough, or (c) just about at the right level.

This, I may add, has been a problem all the way through, and I can only hope that we have hit an acceptable note. It is true that the programmes today are watched by many professional astronomers, no doubt because the field has become so vast that nobody can hope to cover it all; your student of remote galaxies, for instance, need not necessarily know much about Saturn's rings. But we also have to cater for Mrs Jones of Hackney, who is sitting in her armchair watching the programme because she has not had enough energy to go to the set and switch it off. The aim is to capture her interest as well.

Within a day or two of our first foray, letters began to pour in, and most of them were encouraging. I answered them all, and with rare exceptions I still do; the 1908 Woodstock typewriter given to me by my father when I was eight years old (in 1931!) works overtime. Mind you, there are occasions when I have been baffled. One early correspondent wrote to me saying that he had enjoyed hearing me talk about comets, and in consequence wanted to buy an Army tank; had I got any? There was also the dear lady who was anxious to communicate with the beings who live on the Moon, and wondered whether it would be possible to send a carrier pigeon there. I suggested using a pigrot — i.e., a bird which was a cross between a carrier pigeon and a parrot; very useful, as it could convey verbal messages.

Initially the BBC had decided to give *The Sky at Night* a trial run for three programmes: April, May and June 1957. By October we were still going, and of course the ascent of Sputnik 1 was sheer bonus so far as we were concerned, because it brought astronomy well and truly into the public eye. Jodrell Bank, called in to play a vital part in the satellite tracking, became known to everyone, and almost overnight Sir Bernard Lovell — without whom the huge radio telescope would never have been built — was transformed from a crazy spendthrift into a national hero.

Early in our planning we had agreed to invite distinguished guests whenever possible, and one of the first was a man who ranks among the greatest astronomers of our age. His name was Harlow Shapley, and it was he who had first measured the size of our star-system or Galaxy.

As I explained in the lead-in to the programme, our Galaxy, with its hundred thousand million stars, is shaped like a double-convex lens, or, more geographically, like two fried eggs clapped together back to back. (My original wish to produce two eggs and sandwich them had been vetoed by Paul Johnstone.) Round the main system are clumps of stars known as globular clusters, all of which are so far away that even their light, travelling at a casual 186,000 miles per second, takes thousands of years to reach us. Shapley had been able to measure the distances of these clusters, by using special stars which 'give away' their real luminosities by the way in which they behave. He was then able to establish that a ray of light would take around 100,000 years to speed across the Galaxy from one side to the other. He also found that the Sun, with its family of planets, lies well away from the centre of the system, so that we have a lop-sided view.

All this work had been carried out forty years earlier, and it was a great honour to have a first-hand account of it. But I also recall an episode which made the producer wince. With Harlow Shapley and myself was another great astronomer, Bart Bok. We were sitting in a line — one, two, three — and on this occasion we had what is termed a recorded insert. We had filmed a short section of the programme earlier, to avoid an awkward and complicated camera move, and this insert was put into the live transmission as it came out. With malice aforethought, and with thoroughly evil intent, Professors Shapley and Bok changed places for the live transmission, so that when we came to the insert they flicked to and fro in a bewildering manner. By the time that Paul and I found out what they had done, it was too late . . .

Alas, both Harlow and Bart are dead now. They were splendid people as well as famous astronomers; they are much missed.

Meanwhile, events were moving fast, and we did our best to make the programmes move with them. In particular, we were approaching the time of the first Moon-shots.

The Moon had always been my particular love, and my first scientific paper about it had been published as long ago as 1936, when I had reached the advanced age of thirteen. (It was entitled 'Small Craterlets in the Mare Crisium'.) I suppose I became Moon-minded because even a small telescope can show a vast amount of detail there; also, before the 1950s or thereabouts, professional astronomers in general were profoundly uninterested in it, so that lunar mapping was left to amateurs such as myself. But as soon as the Space Age began,

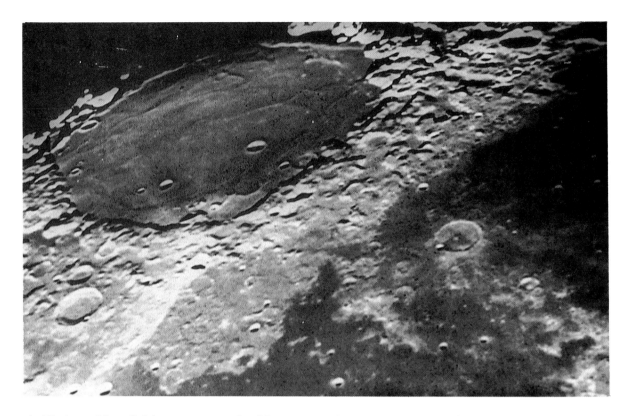

▲ *The lunar Mare Crisium, a small but distinct 'sea' easily visible with the naked eye. It lies near the edge of the Moon as seen from Earth, but, luckily for me, was also shown on the first Lunik 3 picture of the Moon's far side.*

the Moon started to assume a new importance. During 1957 and 1958 the American space-rockets were, frankly, unreliable; they were always liable to explode, fizzle out, or depart in the wrong direction (hence the well-known Cape Canaveral count, a bowdlerized version of which ran '10–9–8–7–6–5–4–3–2–1— *bother*'!) The Russians were having better luck, and in 1959 they launched three unmanned lunar probes.

Lunik 1 was the first. In January it by-passed the Moon, and sent back useful information, such as the news that the Moon has no magnetic field, and your ordinary compass will not work there (remember that next time you are tramping across the Sea of Tranquillity). Then came Lunik 2, in September. It was launched on the 12th of the month, and was scheduled to crash-land on the 13th. By now *The Sky at Night* was fairly well established, and we were able to mount the first of many 'special' programmes, so that on the evening of 12 September we were ready to go.

In a very minor way I had myself been involved in the purely scientific research. As I have said, I was a Moon-mapper; the Russians had asked me to send them my results, which I had done; and they were very good about keeping me abreast of the latest developments. A Soviet astronomer happened to be in London, and although I had never met him it seemed to be a good idea to call him in. Paul agreed. A hasty message was sent, and we were assured that our visitor would turn up on schedule.

Naturally, we were 'live', but when the programme started there was no sign of the Russian. Unfortunate, I thought, but perhaps he would appear; if not, then I would have to manage without him. After a couple of minutes, when I was well launched into a description of what we expected Lunik 2 to accomplish, I saw a newcomer being ushered in by the floor manager and his assistant. As they approached, the floor manager held up a message for me to read. It was only then that I realized, with a feeling of horror, that our Russian guest spoke not one word of English!

What was I to do? I did some quick thinking, and decided to gamble. I put a question, clearly enunciating the word 'Lunik' and pointing to a map of the Moon. He answered in Russian. For all I knew he might have been describing life on a collective farm in Omsk, but I turned to the camera and said what I hoped he was saying about Lunik. I put another question: again he answered; again I said what I hoped was right, after which I thanked him and then finished the programme on my own.

In the event, Lunik 2 crash-landed not far from the lunar crater which we call Archimedes. It carried no instruments and

▼ *With cosmonaut Colonel Valeri Bykovsky. He did speak English, though he did not say a great deal.*

19

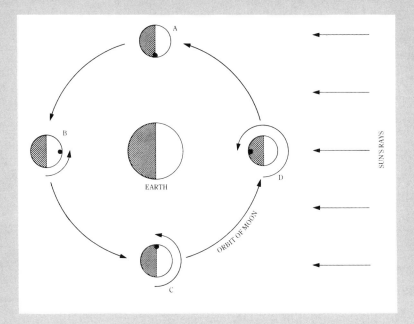

▶ *The dot on the Moon's surface, though always appearing central, shows how the Moon rotates.*

sent back no close-range data, but at least it bridged the Earth–Moon gap, so that it has its place in scientific history. Meanwhile, I waited in fear and trepidation for the reactions of listeners who could speak Russian. They never came. Whether I guessed right I still do not know, but presumably I must have been somewhere near the mark.

The third Russian probe of 1959 was Lunik 3, which began its journey on 4 October, exactly two years after the flight of Sputnik 1. This time I had all the information I needed, because I was involved more as an astronomer than as a television presenter. If you will bear with me, I must say a little here about the way in which the Moon behaves, because it was an essential part of our programme that month.

The Moon is much the closest natural body in the sky. Its mean distance from us is less than a quarter of a million miles, and in my somewhat ancient Ford Prefect car I have covered a distance greater than that, though admittedly not very quickly.[2] The Moon goes round the Earth once in just over 27 days. It spins on its axis in precisely the same time, so that it keeps the same face turned towards us permanently, and from Earth there is a part of the lunar surface which we can never see. In the studio, I demonstrated this by using a chair to represent the Earth, while my head represented the Moon. I then walked round the chair, turning so as to keep my face turned chairward all the time. As I explained, anyone sitting on the chair would

---

[2] *Actually, the mileometer registers 650,000 miles. I may add that a little while ago, when I was driving at top speed up a steep hill near my home, I was passed by a dog.*

never have seen the back of my neck, and 'sitting' on the Earth we never see the back of the Moon. There is no mystery about this — tidal friction over the ages has been responsible — but it was infuriating for astronomers not to know anything definite about so large an area of the Moon. Lunik 3 was designed to go on a round trip, and send back pictures of the uncharted regions.

As the Moon moves, it seems to 'tip' slightly from side to side over a period of several days, for reasons which need not concern us at the moment. The Russians wanted maps of the areas near the lunar limb or edge, which are so foreshortened that they are difficult to study. The Moscow authorities had elected to use some of my maps, which is why they were so willing to keep me posted.

By sheer luck we had a programme scheduled for the evening of 26 October, the very time when we expected to receive the first pictures of the Moon's far side. At the appointed time we went on the air, and I began by describing what we hoped to find out. The Moon, I said, was an airless, mountainous, cratered world; there was no real reason to expect that the far side would be basically different from the hemisphere we knew, but there might always be surprises in store. I even quoted the rhyme allegedly written by a housemaid who had been in the service of a well-known astronomer:

O Moon, lovely Moon with the beautiful face,
Careering throughout the bound'ries of space,
Whenever I see you, I think in my mind
Shall I ever, O ever, behold thy behind?

Meanwhile, unknown to me, the first pictures had arrived in London. The Russians had kept their promise. A BBC messenger was waiting; he grabbed the pictures, jumped on his motor-cycle, and drove to Lime Grove at a rate which would certainly not have met with the approval of the traffic police. Five minutes into the programme, I had a message from Paul Johnstone in the gallery: 'First pictures of the Moon's far side coming up on your screen in thirty seconds. Scrap what we'd planned. Do it off the cuff. Good luck!'

It was a tremendous moment, and I knew that I was about to see something I had wanted to see all my life. I took the audience into my confidence. 'I don't know what's going to come up,' I said, 'but it's bound to be exciting . . . There it is. Look at that!'

Frankly, it was not eye-catching, because as I realized, the Lunik pictures had been taken over 40,000 miles from the Moon's surface, and there were almost no shadows, since the Sun, the rocket and the Moon were almost lined up, giving the equivalent of full-moon illumination. However, I was able to recognize one feature, the small but well-formed plain known as the Mare Crisium or Sea of Crises, because it can be seen from Earth. As soon as I had my bearings, I was able to give what I hope was an intelligible commentary. We had been right in saying that the far side of the Moon was just as cratered, rough and barren as the familiar side. The green fields and little furry animals which had been so vividly described by the flying-saucer enthusiasts were conspicuous only by their absence.

All in all, I have to admit that the Lunik 3 programme remains one of *The Sky at Night* highlights so far as I am concerned. The timing was fortuitous; whether we would have

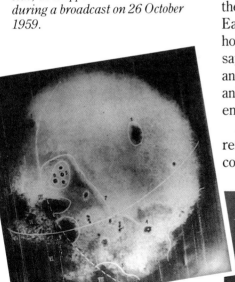

▼ *The Moon from Lunik 3. The very first picture of the Moon's far side, as it appeared on the screen during a broadcast on 26 October 1959.*

▶ *Announcing the first pictures of the Moon's far side. This picture was taken in the studio — unknown to me at the time — just as I had had the message that the first Lunik 3 picture was about to appear on the screen.*

obtained a special programme I do not know, because all the news desks were waiting to cover the story, and it was sheer luck that we happened to be transmitting at exactly the right time.

I thought that the Russians would follow up their triumph quickly, but for some time there was a lull, and it was April 1963 before they tried again. Lunik 4, I fear, was not so successful as its predecessors, as we found out to our cost.

The aim, as the Russians had told me, was to land a capsule on the Moon gently enough to avoid its being destroyed. It could then transmit messages direct from the lunar surface. We mounted a special programme, and made quite elaborate arrangements. We had a telephone link with Moscow, a radio link with Sir Bernard Lovell at Jodrell Bank, and cameras attached to large telescopes in Brighton and at the Royal Observatory, Edinburgh — the idea being to get the latest news from Moscow, listen in to the signals from Jodrell Bank, and then survey the landing area from Brighton, Edinburgh or both. We had a live transmission lasting for an hour and a half.

Do you know those times when absolutely everything goes wrong? It was so on this occasion. Nobody in Moscow knew anything; nobody at Jodrell Bank could hear anything; it was raining in Brighton; it was cloudy in Edinburgh, and moreover Lunik 4 missed the Moon by a full five thousand miles. That was one of my early experiences of what is known in broadcasting jargon as 'padding'. Still, you can't win all the time, and at least we had broken even, with one and a half successes out of three Moon-shots.

▲ *'Lunik 4'. During our abortive programme we received a picture from an Italian photographer who claimed to have recorded the probe. I don't know what it was, but it most certainly wasn't Lunik 4!*

▲ *The nearly full Moon. Note the Mare Crisium, to the left near the limb, which is a 'sea' isolated from the rest and which, to my profound relief, showed up on the Lunik 3 pictures.*

3
The View from Mount Jastrebač

A some time during 1960 I realized that early in the following year there was going to be a total eclipse of the Sun. Of course, I was not the first to tumble to this; all the details had been worked out centuries earlier, but it did seem to give *The Sky at Night* a golden opportunity to try out something really novel, and I went to Paul Johnstone full of enthusiasm. What about a live broadcast, showing the eclipse not once but three times?

Eclipses of the Sun are probably the most spectacular events in all Nature. What happens is that the Moon passes right in front of the Sun, blotting out the brilliant solar disc for a brief period — never as long as eight minutes, and usually much less. The Sun is much larger than the Moon (to be precise, its diameter is 109 times as great), but it is also much farther away, and by a lucky chance the two bodies appear almost exactly the same size in the sky. When the Sun is fully covered the wonderful corona, a pearly mist representing the solar atmosphere, flashes into view against a sky which has darkened enough for stars to be seen.

The trouble is that because the Moon's shadow is only just long enough to touch the Earth, one has to be in just the right place at just the right time. The last total solar eclipse visible

A *Anyone standing in the penumbral shadow will see a partial solar eclipse. Anyone standing in the umbral shadow will see a total eclipse.*

B *When the moon is partially immersed in the umbra we see a partial lunar eclipse. When it is completely in the umbra the eclipse is total.*

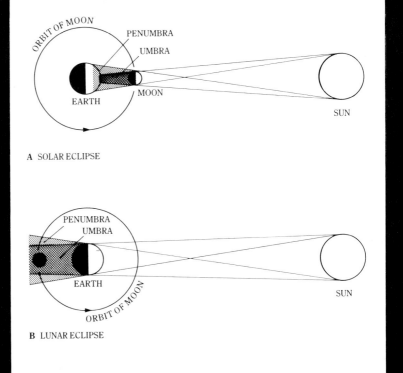

A SOLAR ECLIPSE

B LUNAR ECLIPSE

from anywhere in England was that of June 1927. The track of totality crossed the northern half of the country, but the weather was mainly cloudy; I took no part in the observations myself, partly because I lived in Bognor and partly because I was at the early age of four. However, I did see the total eclipse of 1954, from Sweden, and I was anxious to see another.

The Moon's shadow whips along at a tremendous rate. For the eclipse of 15 February 1961 the line of totality would pass across part of mainland Europe before moving over into Russia; from England the Sun would not be completely hidden, and a small part of the brilliant disc would remain in view, effectively blotting out the corona. We had to go abroad.

My scheme was quite simple. Station three observers along the track, at different points. Totality would occur first in France, then in Italy and then in Yugoslavia, so that if we could enlist the aid of European networks we could have three bites at the solar cherry. Paul agreed, and we set up a conference in Paris to thrash out the details.

I remember that conference well. Various television representatives were there, and when we first met up we found that they were genuinely interested. At one stage I found myself taking the chair during a lively discussion, and I had to concentrate grimly; my French is fairly fluent, even though I speak it with a weird Anglo–Flemish accent (during the war I flew with a Belgian pilot), but I could easily get hold of the wrong end of the stick. One of the representatives was Spanish, and expressed a strong wish to join in. I had to break the sad news that the track of totality did not cross Spain, which made him frown and then ask, plaintively: 'But cannot this be altered?' Unfortunately, shifting the Earth a few million miles was beyond the power even of the BBC.

We also had a rather sceptical and formal Italian delegation. Before lunch the discussions became somewhat sterile, and this was a pity, because Italy was a vital part of our intended chain of stations. Luckily, the Conference president, a Dane named Eddie (what his surname was I have no idea; I doubt whether I ever knew it), had the answer. He took me aside, and gave me some sage advice. 'Take these gentlemen out,' he said, 'and give them plenty to drink.' I must admit that these were not his exact words — they were couched in much more basic Anglo-Saxon — but the advice was good, and I followed it. When we returned in mid-afternoon, things were much better. Indeed, the Italian producer went so far as to suggest that the best way to time the eclipse was to let some lions loose in St Peter's Square and see how many people they ate during totality. By the time we returned to London, everything was more or less fixed.

Why, you may ask, are total eclipses so important? Actually they are less so now than they used to be, thanks to advances in space research; but this was 1961, not 1987, and totality gave the only real chance to study the Sun's corona. The Sun itself has been described, quite appropriately, as a gigantic nuclear furnace, shining because of reactions going on deep inside it; even the bright surface is at a temperature of nearly 6000 degrees Centigrade, and things are even more torrid lower down (I will have more to say about this later). Outside the bright surface comes what is called the chromosphere, which cannot be seen with the naked eye except when the Moon is obliging enough to act as a screen; in the chromosphere are masses of red hydrogen gas which are termed prominences, and which can shift around at amazing speeds. Then, still farther out, comes the corona, made up of almost incredibly thin gas. Sometimes the coronal streamers reach out across the sky, but without an eclipse they cannot be seen at all from the Earth's surface, because they are completely drowned by the blueness of the sky.

What interested astronomers most was, perhaps, the high temperature of the corona, which amounts to more than a million degrees. Yet what astronomers mean by 'temperature' is not what we normally mean by 'heat', and depends upon the velocities at which the various particles move. The faster the speeds, the higher the temperature; but in the corona the particles are so thinly spread that the 'heat' would be quite inadequate to fry an egg. In the studio I demonstrated this by comparing a firework sparkler with a red-hot poker. Each spark of the firework was 'white-hot', but had so little mass that I had no problem in holding the firework in my hand — though I drew the line at grasping the poker, which was only red-hot but was also much more substantial.

We used to think that the high temperature of the corona was due to sound-waves surging up from below. Today we are more inclined to believe that it is due to magnetic effects. Anyway, it was interesting to laymen as well as astronomers, and totality itself would be well worth televising.

The resulting programme was, I feel, a success, particularly since so far as I know it was the first time that anything of the kind had been attempted. On the other hand, there were some curious hitches, and not one of our three stations worked out entirely according to plan.

We enlisted the aid of two highly experienced helpers, Dr Hugh Butler of the Royal Observatory, Edinburgh, and my old friend Colin Ronan, the scientific historian. Hugh was dispatched to St Michel in southern France, where there is a major observatory — fortunately, right on the track of totality (which, incidentally, can never be more than 169 miles wide, this being the diameter of the Moon's shadow cast on the surface of the Earth). Colin went to Florence, and my destination was the top of Mount Jastrebač in Yugoslavia. Hugh would see totality first; then, a few minutes later, Colin; and finally me. We did our best to set up an extra station in Russia, but this fell through, because apparently there were no facilities available, and we were met with a polite and regretful 'Niet'.

From England the eclipse was no more than 90 per cent total, but we could hardly leave ourselves out, and another old friend, Henry Brinton, volunteered to go up in an aircraft above the clouds to broadcast a commentary. It was all most exciting, and as 15 February drew near we had high hopes. By that time I was already in Yugoslavia, so that it was only later that I learned the full details about what had happened. Paul Johnstone, in the Lime Grove studio, was in sole charge.

Henry opened the programme from around 20,000 feet. This went well, and although we could show no pictures the commentary was excellent. Then the centre of attention switched to St Michel, where Hugh Butler was ready and waiting.

This was Hitch No.1. The cameras went 'live'; there was the Sun, and at the appointed time the totality began, with the sky darkening and the corona flashing into view. Of course, this was still in the black-and-white era, but it was still dramatic. Unfortunately, no commentary came through; Hugh was seen on the screen, clearly talking in animated fashion, but not a sound could be heard. Subsequently we found out why. Hugh's commentary went from his mouth to the cameras, from the cameras to the Observatory, from the Observatory to the main transmitter in Milan, from Milan to London, from London to Lime Grove, and thence to the studio — where everything would have been fine if only the technician had remembered to plug it in! With admirable presence of mind, Paul switched to a standby commentary, and prepared to go over to Florence.

This time we had both sound and vision, with Colin giving a graphic description of the scene as totality approached. 'The light is fading,' he said. 'It's impressive, and there is a deathly hush everywhere.' At that moment the last segment of the Sun vanished, and the assembled crowd let out a 'Waaaaaah!' which could probably have been heard in Lime Grove even without the help of a transmitter.

Over in Yugoslavia I was having problems of my own, and because of the failure of my radio link with the Milan station I was completely out of touch. I had no idea whether or not we were on the air, or know whether either of the first two broadcasts had been successful. I felt distinctly isolated.

▲ Ascending Mount Jastrebač. So far as I can remember, I was helping to push the oxen up the steep, snowy track.

Mount Jastrebač is a fairly high peak, not far from the town of Niš (pronounced Neesh). I was the only Englishman in the party, though there were various astronomers from other countries, some there as broadcasters and others as pure scientists. The reasoning was that the cloud-level was likely to be low, so that if we went to the mountain-top — where there was a small radio station — we would probably have a clear sky. In fact the cloud-layer was high, and we were immersed in it. There was also the complication that the Yugoslav director was a man with Ideas, about which I was blissfully ignorant. Our equipment had been taken up the mountain trail in carts pulled by oxen (at least in theory; so far as I can remember, we spent part of the journey pushing the oxen), and the director decided to introduce a Nature note. It is said that when the sky darkens at totality, animals are fooled into believing that night has fallen, and go to sleep. Therefore, why not turn the cameras on the oxen at the moment of totality, and show them dozing peacefully off?

I was unaware of this, because there were linguistic difficulties. I had to talk French to a Belgian astronomer, who relayed it in German to the Yugoslav director, who in turn passed it on to the cameraman in Serbo-Croat. At the preliminary discussions we had literally stood in a circle, playing what was once known as the children's game of 'Whispers', and it was a cumbersome procedure by any standards; I only hoped that it would work.

Five minutes before the vital moment we were still in cloud, and it looked as though we would see nothing at all, but at least it would be obvious when totality occurred; the light-level would drop abruptly. It had been arranged that I should begin my commentary three minutes early — by that time, totality in Italy was over — and all I could do was to start talking and pray that I was being heard. As I later found, Paul was staring at the screen, more or less gnawing his nails, and hoping that I would appear on schedule. To his immense relief, I did. Unfortunately, the Sun didn't; cloud-cover was complete, but there were signs of an approaching break, and I calculated that if all went well it might arrive in time.

Then, abruptly, the light faded. 'Totality is almost upon us,' I said, 'and everything is getting very dark . . . ' It was then that the director switched the cameras on to the group of oxen. Just to make sure that everyone could see them nicely, he floodlit the brutes. Naturally, they simply chewed the cud (if that is what oxen do) and looked stupid. I made a gesture which could not be misinterpreted even in Serbo-Croat, and we got back to the Sun.

We were fortunate. The length of totality was less than three

◄ *Just before totality on Mount Jastrebač; with Rudi Kühn, I am testing equipment.*

► *Transmission from Mount Jastrebač during the 1961 eclipse. It was cold enough for me to wear my Icelandic helmet. At the time I had no idea that I was being photographed; totality was almost upon us.*

minutes, but with about fifty seconds to go the clouds broke; there was the corona, looking glorious, and I was able to describe it. As the Moon edged away from the solar disc we saw the brilliant flash of what is called the diamond-ring effect — the first sliver of sunlight reappearing — and then the light flooded back over the mountain. Almost at once the clouds closed in once more, but I felt well satisfied.

I ended my broadcast five minutes later, still without the slightest idea of whether I had been heard or not. It took us several hours to pack up, and several more to make our way down the mountain to the little village at the bottom. We went into the only pub, where we proceeded to celebrate by drinking a great deal of slivovitz, the local plum brandy which is, believe me, somewhat strong. Finally we saw what we thought to be two jeeps approaching to take us back to Niš. Actually there was only one, but it served, and I was able to call Paul Johnstone, who told me — to my relief — that the programme had been carried through.

At the time it was traumatic, but at least it was a new departure for television, and was also the first of our really ambitious expeditions in *The Sky at Night* story. Since then we have covered several more eclipses, but I will always remember that one best — particularly the sight of those darned oxen blinking stupidly into the glare of the floodlights.

4
The Famous Fiftieth

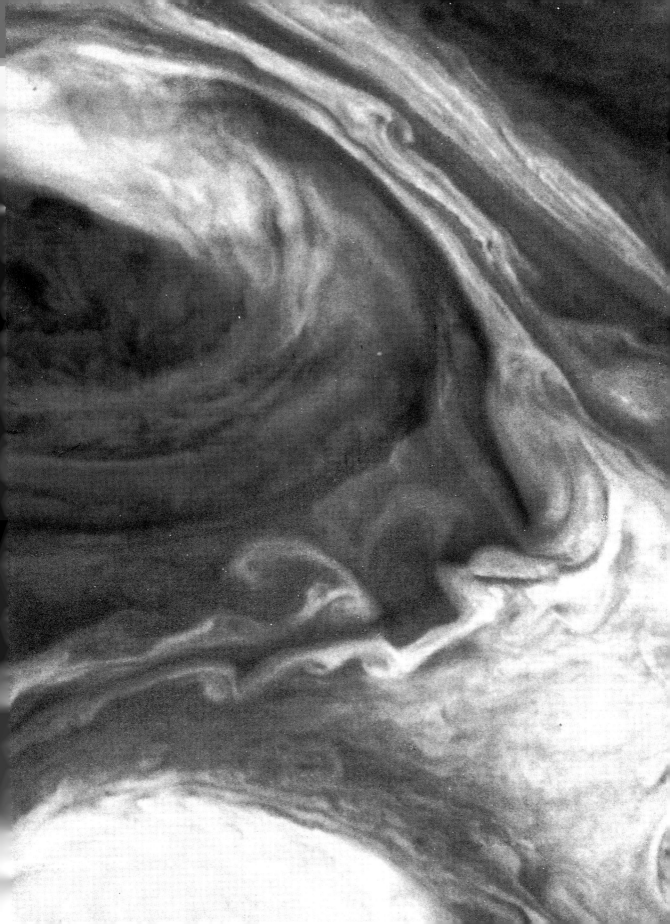

1961 had begun in fine style, and despite the alarms of the eclipse everyone seemed to be well satisfied. Then, on 12 April, came a truly epoch-making event. Major Yuri Gagarin, of the Soviet Air Force, was launched in his spacecraft Vostok 1, and made a complete circuit of the Earth above the top of the main atmosphere, so becoming the first cosmonaut in history.

This gave us a problem. At an early stage we had decided to keep *The Sky at Night* as a purely astronomical programme, bringing in space research only when it was highly relevant. I had a shrewd idea that if we tried to take in all the space missions, astronomy as such would be crowded out, and I am now sure that I was right. Thus, to look ahead, we gave full coverage to the lunar and planetary missions, leaving rockets and space-stations to the news programmes. But we could not ignore Gagarin, and I was able to talk to him about his experiences, though not until some time after his flight into space. Tragically, it was his only one; he was killed in 1968 in an ordinary aircraft crash.

Before Vostok, nobody had any real idea of how the human body would react. There had been several causes for misgiving. First, it had been seriously suggested that any capsule venturing above the atmospheric screen would be battered to pieces by meteorites, a danger which, happily, has proved to be much less severe than was previously thought. Secondly, the air shields us from harmful short-wave radiations from the Sun, and above a height of a few tens of miles this screen is withdrawn. Thirdly, and most menacing of all, there was the problem of zero gravity, or weightlessness. Would a space-traveller be disoriented, or even violently and constantly sick?

Even today, people often have wrong ideas about weightlessness. It is tempting to believe that it is due to 'getting out of gravity', but this is something that can't be done; in theory the Earth's gravitational field is infinite, though of course it weakens with increasing distance. The real cause of zero g is quite different, as I demonstrated in the studio by a simple experiment. I took a book, and on it I placed a coin. 'When I hold the book,' I said, 'the coin is pressing down on it, so that with reference to the book the coin is "heavy". Now, I'm going to drop the book.' I did. 'As the coin falls, the book falls away from underneath it. During the descent, then, the coin ceases to press upon the book, and with reference to the book it has become weightless. The same applies to a space-traveller. He is represented by the coin, and his vehicle by the book. When

◄ (previous page) Jupiter's Red Spot, taken from Voyager. This photo, of course, is later than the events described in this chapter.

► Yuri Gagarin, the first of all spacemen.

they are moving in the same direction at the same rate, the astronaut is no longer pressing on his craft, so that he has no sensation of weight. Even Jules Verne, in his classic story *From the Earth to the Moon*, had got it wrong.

Gagarin's journey disposed of several dreaded bogeys. He did not feel sick (though admittedly several later travellers did); he was not blasted by meteorites or seared by lethal rays, and he did not lose his sense of balance. Indeed, he told me that zero *g* was rather comfortable.

Other missions followed, and we covered them when we thought it necessary, but meantime we were preparing for the first of our anniversaries: the fiftieth *Sky at Night*, due in September 1961. To mark the occasion, we decided to take a risk. Nobody had ever shown planets direct on television, so why not try it, and brave the chance of cloud?

Both the giant planets, Jupiter and Saturn, were visible in the evening sky, because they had been at opposition in the previous July. (When a planet is at opposition, it is on the far side of the Earth with respect to the Sun, so that it is then directly opposite to the Sun in the sky and is well placed for observation.) We needed a powerful telescope. The main instrument in my own observatory at that time, at East Grinstead, was a reflector with a 12½-inch mirror; it was optically excellent, and still is, but it was not clock-driven, so that for television it was useless. As the Earth rotates, the sky seems to move round, carrying everything with it. Unless the telescope is driven so as to follow this movement, the target object will shift quickly out of view. We wanted something more elaborate, and we called in George Hole, a professional instrument-maker, who lived in Brighton and had a massive 24-inch reflector in the open air. It looked like a huge gun, but it

▶ *George Hole's 24-in reflector at Brighton, 1958. This was the telescope used for our Fiftieth Programme. You can see what I mean when I liken it to a huge gun.*

was very suitable for our purpose. Moreover, in September there was a spell of clear weather, and we felt suitably encouraged.

We first had to work out just how the television camera could be adapted to fit the telescope — something which is easy enough now, and has been done many times, but was far from easy in 1961, when television equipment was relatively primitive. I do not pretend to be a technician in any sense of the term, but the BBC team was quite confident, and during the week before the programme we carried out a series of tests which proved to be most satisfactory. Despite the lack of colour, both Jupiter and Saturn were impressive on our monitors. Saturn, with its glorious ring-system, was particularly lovely, and Jupiter's cloud belts were striking; we even saw the four large Jovian satellites, which we now know to be fascinating worlds but about which we knew little at the time.

The giant planets are quite unlike the Earth. They are large — Jupiter is over 80,000 miles in diameter, Saturn over 70,000 — and they are not solid and rocky; their surfaces are made up of gas, chiefly hydrogen, and they are always changing. Jupiter shows its celebrated Great Red Spot, which is a vast oval with a surface area greater than that of the Earth, and which has been

▲ *Jupiter's Great Red Spot, seen from 5,700,000 miles by Voyager. It is whirling round, and dominates all that part of the planet.*

▼ *Enlarged view of the Red Spot, from Voyager. This picture always reminds me of wallpaper!*

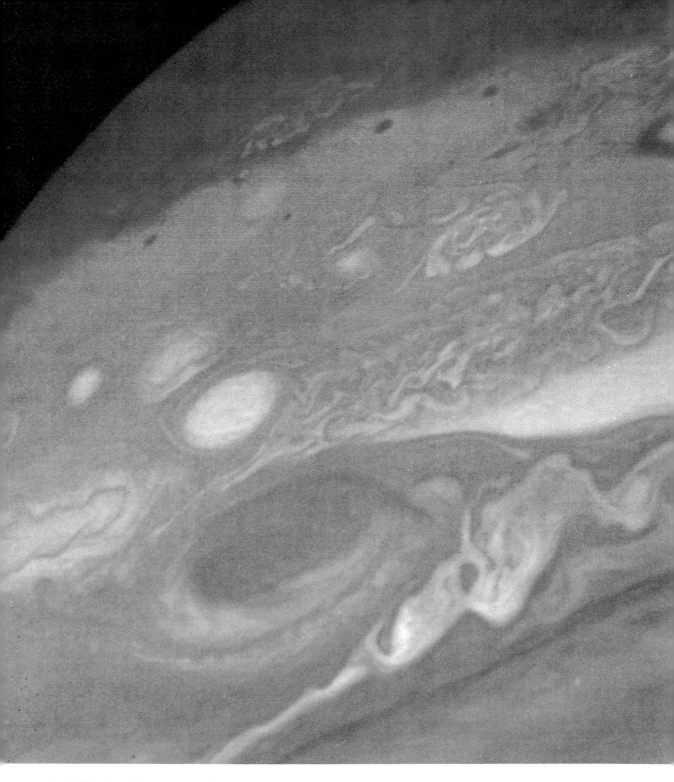

▲ *Jupiter, from Voyager; note the bright zones, the cloud-belts, and the Great Red Spot, which has turned out not to be a floating object as suggested by Peek (remember the egg!).*

under observation ever since the seventeenth century. In 1961 we had no real idea what it was, and it was often believed to be a solid or semi-solid body floating in the Jovian gas. Sometimes it disappears for a while, and may be absent for a few months or even a few years, but it always comes back. Moreover, it drifts about in longitude, so that clearly it could not be attached to any solid core. In the programme before our Fiftieth, I had even given a demonstration of a possible cause of its behaviour, basing myself on a theory due to Bertrand Peek, one of the most famous amateur observers of the time. I must digress for a moment to tell you what happened, because it was directly relevant to our experiment a month later.

According to Peek, the Spot's visibility or invisibility depended upon the changing density of the gas in which it was floating. Peek had likened this to the behaviour of an egg dropped into a vase of water. The egg will sink to the bottom, but if you make the water denser by adding salt the egg will rise to the top. Therefore, said Peek, the Spot is visible only when the surrounding gas is comparatively dense.

I produced a vase, filled it with water, and inserted the egg, which sank. 'Now,' I said, 'I will add salt, and as the water becomes denser the egg will bob up.' I added salt — and salt — and salt; that infernal egg never did rise, though on tests both before and after the transmission it worked perfectly. Don't ask me why it remained obdurate on that one occasion; I never found out!

Back to the Fiftieth . . . We had a quarter of an hour on the air. With five minutes to go, the sky was brilliantly clear, and we had Saturn in view. One minute to go, and the clouds came over. We swung round to Jupiter; clouds covered that too. For the next fifteen minutes we swung the telescope in all directions. 'Over there, George — quickly!' 'Totally obscured.' 'Try there, then — Saturn's visible!' 'Total obscuration.' I padded desperately, and as our air time drew to a close we made a final effort; the telescope hurtled down towards me, and I leaped aside just in time. We saw absolutely nothing. Five minutes later, and there wasn't a cloud to be seen. It was a classic case of what astronomers call Spode's Law: If things *can* go wrong, they *do*. (The identity of Spode, I may add, remains shrouded in mystery.)

Well, it was a good try; at least we had shown that it could be done, clouds permitting, and since then we have been successful more often than not. Years later, when I set up my 15-inch clock-driven telescope at Selsey, we showed Saturn really well, in colour. But I must admit that the Fiftieth *Sky at Night* turned out to be a comedy show, even though it wasn't intended to be.

Incidentally, we now know that Peek's theory is wrong. The Red Spot is not a solid body; it is a whirling storm — a phenomenon of Jovian 'weather' — and the redness is probably due to phosphorus welling up from the cloud-layer below. That was something we learned from the Voyager spacecraft of the late 1970s, but at the time of our Fiftieth the idea of sending a probe out to the giant planets still seemed very futuristic.

5
The
Martian
Cactus

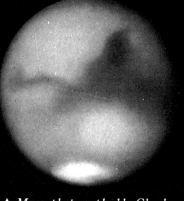

▲ *Mars, photographed by Charles Capen at the Lowell Observatory. The V-shaped feature, the Syrtis Major, was once thought to be an old sea-bed filled with vegetation, but is now known to be a plateau.*

uring our *Sky at Night* planning we have always tried to be as topical as we can. In particular, we like to concentrate upon things that the viewer can actually see for himself, and bright planets are always attractive. After our initial fiasco with Jupiter and Saturn (to say nothing of the recalcitrant egg) we begn to think about Mars, and we looked round for a new angle.

To the naked eye Mars appears as a red blob. Binoculars show it as a rather larger red blob. You need a telescope of considerable size to see much on its surface, but with adequate power you can make out the white polar caps, the dark markings, the ochre areas and occasional clouds. Though Mars is farther away from the Sun than we are (over 140,000,000 miles on average, as against our 93,000,000), and is colder, it is in some respects not too unwelcoming. The main problem is that it is small and light-weight — you would need ten bodies the mass of Mars to equal one Earth — and it pulls much more feebly than our world. Go there, and you will have only one-third of your Earth weight. This strikes me as an attractive prospect (I decline to say what my Martian weight would be), but it also means that much of the planet's original atmosphere has leaked away into space, because Mars was unable to hold it down. Neither can there be any oceans, lakes or rivers there.

All this we knew in the early 1960s. We hoped for new information when, in November 1962, the Russians launched their first Mars probe. Unfortunately, it failed. At that stage the Soviet planners were having severe problems with long-range communications and control; they could put spacecraft into the correct orbits, but keeping track of them was another matter. Mars-1 transmitted obediently for some time, but then went silent, and was never located again. Presumably it is still whirling round the Sun, having been transformed into a dead and entirely useless member of the Solar System.

Thrown back on our own resources, we decided to make our own investigation into the possibility of life on Mars. The idea was not new. Less than half a century earlier the American astronomer Percival Lowell had been making drawings of what he believed to be artificial Martian canals, built by intelligent beings to provide a planet-wide irrigation system; lacking seas, the only water-supply would presumably come from the polar ice-caps, so that according to Lowell the waters were drawn off and then pumped through to the warmer regions near the equator. Just what the 'Martians' were like he did not pretend to know. For all he could tell, they might have three heads and green tentacles; but if they could really set up such an elaborate system they would have to be brainy.

Some writers even speculated as to how we could talk to the

Martians if we managed to establish contact. Certainly it would be rather daunting to meet an alien who greeted you with a friendly wave and a cry of 'Wzjgdd gxblzk hxtrboz!' — but the first thing to establish was whether advanced life on Mars could exist at all. Could *The Sky at Night* help?

It was worth a try. (After all, as recently as 1903 there had been a large cash prize offered in France for the first successful contact with beings from another world, Mars being specifically excluded as much too easy.) We needed a microbiologist, and

▼ *The Martian Scientist, showing that life on Earth is impossible owing to the dense atmosphere and the abundance of water. I think I had disguised myself just sufficiently!*

fortunately we were able to enlist the aid of another of my friends, Dr Francis Jackson, a microbiologist by profession and an amateur astronomer by inclination. After a preliminary meeting, we decided to set up what was to all intents and purposes a Martian laboratory.

Obviously we needed to know what the conditions on the planet were like, and we had to base ourselves on the latest available information. We knew the gravitational force; as I have said, it was one-third that of Earth, and this was something we could not simulate, so we had to hope that the increased 'weight' of our samples would make no essential difference. We knew the length of the Martian day, just over half an hour longer than ours (to be precise, 24 hours 37 minutes 22·6 seconds). The length of the Martian year — 687 Earth days, or 669 Martian days — did not matter; our experiments were to be fairly short-term. In the middle of the Martian day, on the planet's equator, the temperature could rise to well over 40 degrees Fahrenheit, but the thin atmosphere was known to be very poor at shutting in warmth, so that at midnight the temperature plummeted to around −150 degrees. As I remember saying, any campers on Mars had better be sure to take plenty of winter clothing with them.

There remained the problem of the planet's atmosphere, and this was where we went badly wrong, though at the time we had no chance of doing any better.

Of the presence of an atmosphere round Mars there was no doubt at all. Clouds periodically veil the surface (not rain-clouds; they are more in the nature of dust-storms), and in any case there was ample evidence from that invaluable optical tool, the spectroscope. Just as a telescope collects light, so a spectroscope splits it up, and shows what substances are present in the light-source. For example: look at the spectrum of the Sun, and you will see unmistakeable traces of many common elements, including tin and iron as well as the ubiquitous hydrogen gas. A planet shines by reflected sunlight, and so it shows what is basically a reflected solar spectrum, but any surrounding atmosphere will leave its own particular imprints. Remember, the light we receive from Mars has passed through the planet's atmosphere twice — once on its way from the Sun to Mars, and then again on the outward journey from Mars to Earth.

Careful studies, carried out at the main professional observatories (including Lowell's, at Flagstaff in Arizona) had indicated that the main gas round Mars was nitrogen, which of course makes up 78 per cent of the air that you and I are breathing. With Earth, most of the rest of the atmosphere is oxygen. We did not expect much oxygen on Mars, but we did anticipate a good deal of the heavy, unbreathable gas carbon dioxide.

Certainly there was no reason to expect anything poisonous, but on the debit side the density was likely to be low. The favoured value at ground-level was about 85 millibars. Translated into everyday terms, this meant that the atmospheric pressure at the surface of Mars was about the same as that in the Earth's air at a height of 52,000 feet.

Everest, our highest mountain, is less than 30,000 feet above sea-level, and even there climbers find it extremely difficult to breathe without using special masks, so that there was never any chance that future explorers would be able to go to Mars, step outside their spacecraft, and take deep, refreshing breaths in the daytime cool. But lower forms of life are much hardier, and a nitrogen atmosphere of this type would be quite suitable for organisms such as algae. We even anticipated lowly vegetation. Why should not the dark areas be old seabeds covered with, for example, lichen or moss?

There was in fact good reason to believe that this might be so. The dust-storms would otherwise spread material everywhere, and hide the dark regions, so that the whole of Mars would assume a uniform ochre-red colour. But, as had been pointed out by the Estonian astronomer Ernst Öpik, plants could push the dusty stuff away and poke through quite happily.

One thing we did not expect to find was any advanced life. Not even insects could survive under Martian conditions. At a public lecture just before our first programme I even stated that 'on Mars we may find lowly plants, but nothing so advanced as a cabbage', though the local newspaper subsequently reported me as claiming that 'the nearest approach to Earth-type life on Mars was likely to be the growth of large cauliflowers . . . '

Under Francis's direction, we constructed our Martian laboratory, which took the form of a large airtight cabinet. We filled it with a Martian atmosphere — chiefly nitrogen, with traces of carbon dioxide and other gases which we might reasonably expect — and arranged for an alternation of temperature between 'day' and 'night', using a packing of dry ice (that is to say, solid carbon dioxide; the material you find in an ice-cream seller's barrow). We thought we knew a good deal about the Martian soil, which was a mixture of iron oxides — rust, if you like — and various rocky materials. Then we discussed what organisms we should try.

Cacti seemed to be good candidates. After all, they can survive in all manner of improbable places; they need very little water, and in any case we could not rule out the possibility that there might be a water-supply below ground. Cacti are also tolerant of violent temperature fluctuations between day and night. So, in our first programme we produced a cactus, and announced we were about to subject it to Martian conditions.

► *Mars from Mariner 4; the pointer indicates one of the newly found craters.*

The cactus didn't like it. After a single Martian night it looked decidedly limp. When we saw it we all broke into uncontrollable laughter, but we decided that we really could not show it on the programme. I don't want to go into details of why not; I will leave these to your imagination, but suffice to say that had Mrs Whitehouse been around at the time (which she wasn't, of course), she would have objected strongly. So the cactus was relegated to anonymity, and we turned to simpler life-forms.

The results were interesting. Very primitive forms such as algae were uncomfortable after a couple of Martian nights, but some types of bacteria survived, and there were even indications that they might be able to multiply. In our second (and, as it proved, final) programme on the subject, we went so far as to claim that 'if our picture of the Martian surface and atmosphere is reasonably correct, there is a real possibility that some terrestrial bacteria could establish themselves there'.

We felt that we had made a real contribution to science. Our experiment was not the first of its kind, but it had been carried out under strictly controlled conditions, and had been supervised by an expert. We waited for the academic world to acclaim us.

Alas! pride goes before a fall. And within a year or so we

found that we had achieved absolutely nothing.

In November 1964 the Americans launched their second attempted Mars probe, Mariner 4 (its predecessor, Mariner 3, had taken off in the wrong direction, and had joined the ever-increasing swarm of useless artificial planets). On 14 July 1965 Mariner 4 passed within 21,000 miles of Mars, and sent back close-range pictures, showing that instead of being no more than gently undulating, as everyone had expected, the surface was cratered like that of the Moon. Worse, it established that the atmospheric ground-pressure is nothing like as high as we had believed. To reach equivalent density above the Earth, you would have to go up not 52,000 feet, but more like twenty miles. In fact, the situation on the Martian surface is comparable with what we would call a reasonably good laboratory vacuum; and to complete the picture, what atmosphere there is consists not of nitrogen, but of almost pure carbon dioxide.

So the work we had so carefully done was based upon completely erroneous data. Since then we have learned a great deal more, and in the mid-1970s, when the Viking probes made controlled landings on the red Martian deserts, we were able to put the record straight; but it is sad to recall that the sacrifice of that noble, wilting cactus turned out to be in vain.

▼ *Mariner 4, America's first successful Mars probe.*

6

I y not to vise an cial Star

Ar

In the early days of *The Sky at Night* all our studio programmes were transmitted from Lime Grove, in Shepherd's Bush; the Television Centre in Wood Lane had not been built. When we filmed, our 'outside broadcasts' (or OBs) came sometimes from places of special relevance, such as George Hole's observatory, or from my home in East Grinstead. But in 1965 I made one of the only two moves I have made in my adult life, and took on the only professional post I have ever held or ever want to hold. I was invited to become the first Director of the Armagh Planetarium, and I accepted. In June of that year I left Sussex — I admit with great regret — and shifted lock, stock, barrel (and cat) to Northern Ireland.

Armagh is the astronomical centre of the province. It has an old-established observatory, controlled for many years during the last century by the formidable Dr Romney Robinson. He was certainly a man of strong character; when the railway line from Belfast to Newry was being planned, Dr Robinson managed to have it diverted for several miles, because he claimed that the vibration of passing trains would shake his telescopes!

When I went there the observatory director was an old friend of mine, Dr Eric Mervyn Lindsay, who had, incidentally, taken that classic photograph of the Arend-Roland Comet which had ushered in the very first *Sky at Night*. Eric was keen to set up a planetarium, and also keen for me to go there to take on the responsibility. I was initially dubious — years earlier I had declined an invitation to become the first director of the London Planetarium in the Marylebone Road — but eventually I went. It was a challenge, and I rather relished it. It also provided great scope for another experimental television programme.

You probably know the principle of a planetarium. The main instrument is a complicated projector, which throws images of the stars (or anything else you like) on to the inside of a large reflecting dome. During a display the effect is remarkably like the real thing, and it is hard to believe that you are not in the open. Moreover, a planetarium can do things that the actual sky cannot. You can speed up the movements of the planets, and show how they behave; you can reproduce eclipses, comets, meteors, polar lights — the choice is wide. The first planetarium was built at Jena, in what is now East Germany, in 1926, and the basic principles have been unchanged ever since, though naturally the equipment has been improved and elaborated.

I went to Jena to see their planetarium. (On the way back I managed to get a jeep stalled in Checkpoint Charlie, in the Berlin Wall, and was faced with infuriated Germans poking guns into my ribs. I used up my entire stock of the Teutonic language, which amounts to 'Niet sprecken Deutsch. Sauer-

kraut. Donner und blitzen. Das isch all,' and waited until they produced someone who talked French.) I recommended a 40-foot dome for Armagh, and this was accepted.

Which type of projector ought we to buy? It was a straight choice between the German Zeiss, the American Spitz and the Japanese Goto. The Zeiss was prohibitively expensive. The Spitz was cheaper, and was good, but it does look rather like a lavatory cistern, and the Goto was much more elegant, so I was called to Japan to make further investigations. It was my first trip to the Far East, and I enjoyed it, though it did have its awkward moments. I particularly remember staying in a small

▲ *The Armagh Planetarium, 1966. It then consisted only of the actual dome; it has been greatly extended now, with the addition of a major exhibition known as the Lindsay Hall in honour of Eric Lindsay.*

51

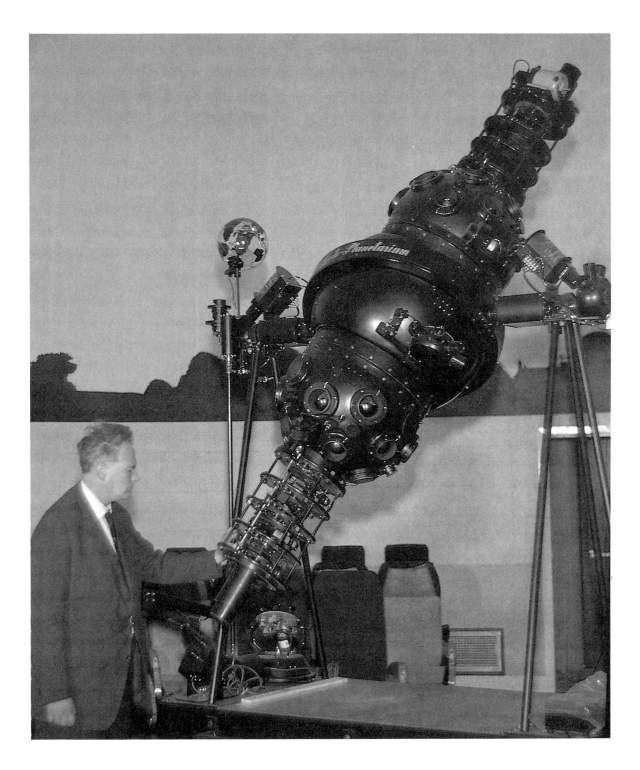

▲ *The original Goto projector at the*
Armagh Planetarium. It worked
well — but don't try to photograph
the Planetarium sky in the way that
we did!

hotel outside Tokyo, where guests were expected to take off their shoes before entering; my shoes are roughly the size of rowing-boats, and when I took them off I was acutely aware of a large hole in my sock. One also has to abandon European clothes, and assume Japanese robes for dinner. The sight of my sweeping down into the restaurant attired in a kimono was rather too much even for the polite Japanese; on me, the kimono looked like a ballet-skirt, and also revealed one of my secrets — i.e. that I am violently knock-kneed and could not possibly stop a pig in a passage.

However, negotiations went well. We acquired a Goto, and before long the building in Armagh was ready. We had the grand opening, attended by many famous Irish politicians and ministers whose names I totally forget, and then we were ready for a

▼ *A* Sky at Night *from Armagh. With me are Paul Johnstone (right) and Dr Eric Lindsay, the Director (centre). In the background is the dome which covers Dr Romney Robinson's telescope, and for which Robinson managed to have the Belfast-Newry railway line diverted.*

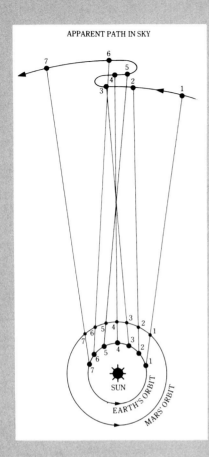

APPARENT PATH IN SKY

Sky at Night programme, the first ever to be broadcast from inside a planetarium so far as I know.

I was happy with the projector — perhaps because I had myself had a major share in designing the plates for it! — and the venture aroused considerable interest. My idea was to instal the cameras and then show the planetarium sky, demonstrating how realistic it was. We could then 'work' the planets — for instance, showing the movements of Mars over a period of weeks; and this may be worth describing here, because it is not easy to appreciate in the real sky since the motions are so slow.

Mars, as we have seen, goes round the Sun at a distance greater than that of the Earth. It shifts against the stars from one night to another, but not with absolute regularity. Sometimes it stops, backtracks for a while, and then stops again before using its usual movement from west to east. Ancient astronomers found great difficulty in explaining this, but it is quite simple. As the Earth 'passes' Mars, the planet will appear to shift for a while in the reverse direction; we call it 'retrograding'. I think the diagram here will show what is meant, and in the planetarium we can speed the process up, making Mars loop in a matter of a minute or two instead of taking weeks.

Patricia Owtram, who had taken over as producer of *The Sky at Night* on Paul Johnstone's elevation to higher office in the BBC, arrived at Armagh complete with a television crew. We set things up, and, a day before the programme was due to be transmitted, we had a trial run. It was then that I realized how

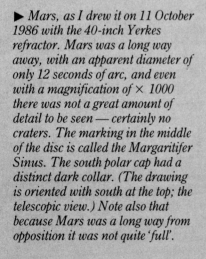

▶ *Mars, as I drew it on 11 October 1986 with the 40-inch Yerkes refractor. Mars was a long way away, with an apparent diameter of only 12 seconds of arc, and even with a magnification of × 1000 there was not a great amount of detail to be seen — certainly no craters. The marking in the middle of the disc is called the Margaritifer Sinus. The south polar cap had a distinct dark collar. (The drawing is oriented with south at the top; the telescopic view.) Note also that because Mars was a long way from opposition it was not quite 'full'.*

unbelievably stupid I had been.

To show anything on a television screen, you need a certain amount of light. Otherwise you will see nothing but blackness, which is not notably informative. But the stars projected on to the inner surface of a planetarium dome are themselves spots of light — and as soon as there is any trace of interior illumination, the stars go out!

This could be mastered today, with modern-type electronic gadgetry, but not in 1965. We did everything we could, and reduced the light-level in the dome to the absolute minimum, but still there were no stars. We even tried to show the planetarium Moon, which looked like a ghostly saucer.

It was no good. All we could salvage was a view of the projector itself, and then use slides and photographs to explain what would have been seen if only we had been able to show it. Things were not so disastrous as might be thought, because there was still much to say, and the idea of a planetarium was not nearly so familiar then as it is now, but I really ought to have known better.

I stayed at Armagh for three years, but at the end of that time I felt that I had done all I had set out to do, and the call of Sussex was strong. I handed over the directorship to my successor (Terry Moseley) and came home, acquiring a house in Selsey which had begun life as a barn and which I have not the slightest desire to leave either now or in the future. One reason for my decision was that as the planetarium grew in popularity, I found it increasingly difficult to get over to London frequently, and with a monthly programme we always have to have at least a couple of pre-transmission meetings.

I recall one episode which may have some bearing on events. I was flying over on a Sunday evening, ready for the programme due for transmission that night. I flew on British United Airways, who, unlike BEA of evil memory, provided an in-flight dinner. I bit on what I thought was a grape; it turned out to be an olive — and there was a horrible snapping sound . . . . I have had a full denture ever since I was in my teens (the result of having to land an aircraft which had been somewhat knocked about by a member of the Luftwaffe, who had taken pot-shots at us in what I thought at the time was a most unfriendly manner). So there was I, due on the air in less than four hours, holding two halves of a top denture.

There was only one answer: Sellotape. I did my best, but I had to speak in a kind of snarl through tightly clenched jaws, and I hardly think that it was one of my best performances. All in all I was glad to get back to Selsey Bill, particularly as the space programme was now in full swing and in *The Sky at Night* we had a great deal to occupy our minds.

7
Stars that didn't shoot

I am sure that you must have seen a meteor or shooting-star at one time or another, though of course not everyone knows what meteors are, and during the flying-saucer craze of the 1950s they were responsible for more reports of space visitations than I could even estimate. It is true that a brilliant meteor can be really spectacular. I have seen quite a number which have outshone the full moon for a few seconds, and have left luminous trails, but they do not persist for long, and they are not nearly so important as they may look. Nearly all of them are much smaller than grapes.

I say this because on the early morning of 17 November 1966 we tried out a new experiment in *The Sky at Night*, and for the first time we invited what is known in television jargon as audience participation. It was not a mere gimmick, because we wanted to collect some useful scientific information as well, and this appeared to be a good way to do it. So if you will bear with me for a few moments, I must give you a brief run-down of what meteor studies are all about.

As I have said, a meteor is not large. The average particle is about the size of a grain of dust, and is moving round the Sun in exactly the same way that we are. For obvious reasons we cannot see it unless it encounters the Earth; it is much too

▼ *An engraving of meteorites seen over Florida.*

small. While it is moving in space there is nothing to brake it, but if it swoops into the top of our atmosphere, at a height of (say) 120 miles or so, it has to push its way through the air-particles. This sets up friction, which in turn produces heat, and the meteor burns away, producing the streak of radiance which we call a shooting-star. By the time it has fallen to a height of about 40 miles above ground-level it has burned away completely, ending its journey in the form of very fine dust.

But, you may ask, how can such a tiny object make so brave a showing? The answer is that it is moving quickly, at a relative speed of up to 45 miles a second. What we see is not the particle itself but the effects it has on the atmosphere during its final headlong dash. To demonstrate friction, I produced a bicycle-pump, and blew up a tyre; when I put my hand on the pump it felt hot. (Not that I could broadcast 'heat', but you can see what I mean. *En passant*, and in quite another context, my old friend Professor Sam Tolansky, FRS, once appeared on television on April the 1st, fried onions in front of the camera, and broadcast smells. The number of people who telephoned to say that they could detect the odour of those onions was quite remarkable.)

Meteors tend to travel round the Sun in shoals, and every time we pass through a shoal of particles we see a shower of meteors. This happens many times in each year, and several dozens of individual showers are listed. The meteors of any particular shower seem to come from one special area of the sky, which is called the shower radiant. This is because they are really travelling through space in parallel paths. To explain this, we took our cameras on to a bridge overlooking a motorway — one of the first; I think it must have been the M1 — and showed how the lanes seemed to diverge from a point near the horizon, which I termed the radiant of the lanes. The photograph given

▼ Radiant Principle; I took this picture from a bridge overlooking the M1, and the lanes seem to meet at their 'radiant' near the horizon, though of course they are in fact parallel.

here was actually taken at the time. I pointed out that cars coming from the distance would seem to diverge from the radiant of the lanes, just as meteors from space will appear to diverge from the radiant of the shower.

I then had a letter from a motoring organization, complaining bitterly that according to my description all the cars and other vehicles would be coming down all the lanes in the same direction, causing something of a traffic crisis. However, I don't think he meant to be taken seriously; the letter was signed 'A. Rhode-Hogg'.

The best time for meteor-watching is August, because during the first fortnight of the month we plough through a rich shoal. The meteors emanate from a radiant in the constellation of Perseus, so that they are known as the Perseids. Go outdoors at any time on a dark, clear night between the end of July and around 17 August, stare upward for a few minutes, and you are almost certain to see a meteor or two. But in 1966 we were in pursuit of a much more erratic shower, the Leonids, which come from the region of Leo, the Lion.

Meteors are 'bits and pieces' left behind by comets, which are untidy things and leave débris in their wake as they move round the Sun. The Leonids are associated with a rather dim comet which need not concern us for the moment; the shoal goes round the Sun in a period of just over 33 years, and the particles are bunched up, so that now and then we see really magnificent displays, while during other years there are practically no Leonids at all. Records of them go back as far as the year 902. There were superb showers in 1799, 1833 and 1866, all in mid-November, but unfortunately the meteors are so light-weight that they are easily pulled around by the gravitational tugs of the planets, and the expected showers of 1899 and 1933 did not materialize. However, there was every hope that the Leonids would be back in force in 1966, and we knew exactly when to expect them: between midnight and 6 a.m. on 17 November. Conditions were scheduled to be ideal, because the Moon was a slender crescent in the evening sky and would be out of the way long before the Leonid maximum. We fully expected to see a display comparable with those of past years, when it was said that for several hours meteors 'fell from the sky like snowflakes', so rapidly that to count them was quite impossible.

I had long discussions with Pat Owtram. Astronomers were very anxious to know the number and brightness of the meteors, and amateurs could make notable contributions if they were told what to do. This also applied to members of the general public. During the October *Sky at Night* we paved the way, and announced that anyone willing to take part would be

sent a special chart upon which the meteor tracks could be recorded. Of course, this involved a certain knowledge of the constellation patterns, but even a vague indication was better than nothing, and simple counts of the numbers were not to be despised, even though they could be no more than approximate in the event of a really rich shower.

Harold Ridley, the Director of the Meteor Section of the British Astronomical Association, joined me for the October programme, and was suitably enthusiastic. At once requests began to flood in. We distributed a grand total of 11,000 charts — one of them is shown here; luckily I kept it — and over 9000

▲ The Leonids that didn't shoot; I am holding the chart, copies of which we sent out to all volunteer helpers.

61

were returned as soon as the shower was over.

One thing we wanted to establish, as accurately as possible, was the ZHR or Zenithal Hourly Rate. This is the number of naked-eye meteors which an observer could expect to see under perfect conditions, with the radiant at the zenith or overhead point. In practice conditions are never perfect, but the average ZHR for the August Perseids works out at around 60, and for the Leonids of 1833 and 1866 it had been more like 200,000. Why should not 1966 be equally good?

We kept an eagle eye on the weather, and through 16 November we were in constant touch with the Met. Office; the BBC News Department was extremely helpful, and put out regular bulletins. Night duly fell. Inevitably, from Armagh the sky was cloudy. (Clouds and rain are the norm in Armagh; it is a constant source of surprise to me that Northern Irish children aren't born with webbed feet and fins.) I could therefore take no practical part in the observations, and was reduced to keeping in touch at the end of a telephone line.

Nothing much happened before 1 a.m., but then I had a call from a man in Kent who had actually seen a Leonid. Skies over England in general were reasonably clear, except in the far north, so that from that point of view there was no cause for complaint, but by 2 a.m. I was starting to have a nasty sinking feeling. We had at least ten thousand watchers on the alert, and if the Leonids failed us my name would be cosmic mud.

Which is exactly what happened . . . Leonids were, to put it mildly, sparse, and seemed to be doing their very best to avoid us. I doubt whether any of our observers saw as many as twenty throughout the whole period between midnight and sunrise. Then the charts came flooding back — most of them totally blank, with occasional streaks which might perhaps indicate the track of a Leonid. There were some relevant comments, too, which I kept on file:

Chatham. Sky clear. No moon. No meteors. What have you done with them?
West Bromwich. Ha, ha, ha. Meteors, my (*censored*).
Carlisle. Couldn't see any meteors, but it was raining all the time; can this be why I missed them?
Falmouth. I never did trust astrologers. Use a crystal ball.
And finally:
Birmingham. As requested, watched the sky from midnight until dawn. Meteors: from the sky — none. From the wife — plenty.

What had gone wrong? Well, it was a question of timing, and it wasn't our fault. The Leonids did appear, but they were twelve hours late. At about midday on the 17th the shower hit Earth, and from parts of America it was fully as glorious as it had been a hundred years earlier. From Kitt Peak, in Arizona, the hourly rate was estimated as well over 100,000, and the sight was truly awe-inspiring. The shower was visible from much of the western hemisphere, but of course it was daylight over Europe, so that we saw virtually nothing. It was another classic case of Spode's Law.

Mind you, our observations were scientifically valuable, because we were able to establish without a shadow of a doubt that the display was brief. The Perseid meteors have been spread all round the orbit of their parent comet; the Leonids are bunched up, and our observers proved that the bunch is of limited size. All in all, the meteor students were satisfied, even though *Sky at Night* viewers weren't.

At least there is always 17 November 1999. We will try again then, and I ask for your help in advance. Keep that night free, but please don't blame me if the Leonids fail once more, and all you can see are aircraft, weather balloons and occasional flying saucers.

◄ *Old woodcut of the great Leonid storm of 1833, when it was said that meteors 'rained down like snowflakes'. It happened again in 1866, and then in 1966, though on the latter occasion we in Britain missed it by several hours — hence the* Sky at Night *embarrassment!*

8
Venus
Observed

▲ *Venus, from the American Pioneer Orbiter. The swirling clouds are shown, looking very lovely — and hiding the raging inferno beneath, which I do not recommend for a week-end trip!*

▼ *The surface of Venus, from Russia's Venera 13 (1982). Part of the spacecraft is shown. The rocks are so hot that they actually glow, and no spacecraft can survive for long.*

Television techniques today are so sophisticated that one needs an effort of the imagination to look back at what may be called the Neolithic Period, before electronics took over. In the early days we had to resort to all manner of dodges, and of course everything was 'live', so that there could be no second chances. Lighting was often a problem, even before the introduction of colour, and on one occasion Paul Johnstone produced a novel solution.

We were demonstrating what are termed stellar proper motions. The stars are so far away that they appear to all intents and purposes stationary with respect to each other, and Orion and the Great Bear look just the same to us as they must have done to Julius Caesar, but given enough time the tiny proper motions become evident. Return to Earth in, say, 50,000 years hence, and the pattern of the Bear will have become distorted, because two of its stars are moving through space in a direction opposite to that of the other five.

We wanted to explain this — but how? Paul thought he knew. We darkened the studio, and enlisted the aid of five girls from a local ballet troupe, who dressed themselves in jet black and carried tiny lamps to represent stars. We positioned them in a way which would produce the Bear pattern as seen from the camera, and then asked two of them to shift slightly, so that the movements of their lamps could be followed. It worked, though I gather that the dancers themselves could also be dimly seen. We had many comments from viewers, and also from my studio guest, who complained that the situation quite put him off his stroke and distracted his attention from theoretical astrophysics!

However, the movement of the Sun's planets is quite apparent, because they are so much closer to us, and after the

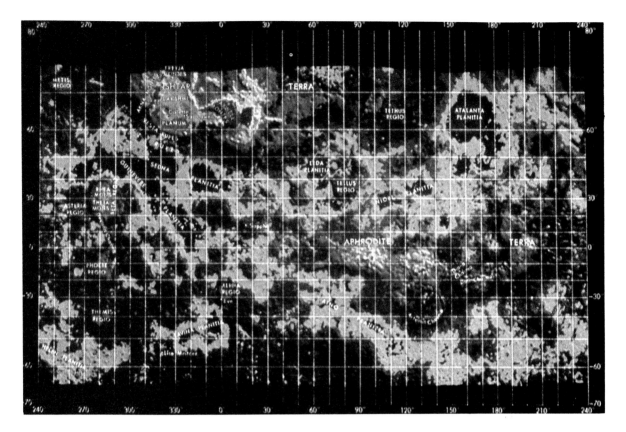

Martian laboratory episode it was time to turn our attention to Venus.

Venus is much the brightest of the main planets, and is also the nearest; it can approach us to within 25,000,000 miles, which is some ten million miles closer than Mars can ever come. It is about the same size as the Earth, but before the Space Age we knew very little about it, because we can never have a direct view of its surface. Unlike its mythological namesake, Venus is always shrouded in protective clothing. There is a dense, all-concealing atmosphere, and the weather there is always cloudy. Our first programme about it outlined the various theories which had been proposed. What was the Planet of Love really like?

According to the early twentieth-century Swedish scientist Svante Arrhenius, Venus was likely to be in the same condition as the Earth was over 200 million years ago, when the Coal Forests were being laid down and even the dinosaurs had yet to make their entry. Because Venus is closer to the Sun than we are, it was obviously going to be hot, but just how hot we didn't then know. Arrhenius pictured swamps, luxuriant vegetation of the fern and horsetail variety, insects such as dragonflies, and huge amphibians, the ancestors of our modern frogs and toads. We even showed a frog as an example of a potential Venusian,

▲ *Radar map of Venus, from the US Pioneer orbiter. The colours are false — red highest, blue lowest — and do not indicate lands and seas. Seas on Venus would not be very plausible at a temperature of nearly 1000 degrees F!*

though it showed very little interest in the proceedings and merely wanted to get back to its pond.

Alternatively, Venus could have been a watery world, with almost no dry land at all. It was known that the atmosphere was made up chiefly of carbon dioxide, and if there were any seas they would have been fouled — bearing in mind that water containing carbon dioxide is nothing more nor less than soda-water. The idea of soda-water oceans was intriguing, though, as I pointed out, the chances of finding any whisky to mix with it were effectively nil.

Thirdly, Venus could have been a raging dust-desert, with a surface temperature much too high for liquid water to exist. I may say that in 1962 this latter picture was shown to be the right one; America's Mariner 2 by-passed the planet, and promptly disposed of Arrhenius's frogs as well as the soda-water sea. But while on the subject of Venus, there were two other programmes about that time which may be worth mentioning here, particularly since the first of them involved more audience participation.

Obviously, the Sun can light up only half of Venus at any one time, so that one hemisphere of the planet shines while the other does not. When Venus is almost between the Sun and the Earth, its dark side faces us; the planet is 'new', and cannot normally be seen at all. (The diagram should make this clear; the phases are due to the same basic cause as those of the Moon, though of course the Moon revolves round the Earth and not round the Sun.) As the planet moves on, a little of the sunlit side is turned towards us, and Venus appears as a crescent in the evening sky. It changes slowly into a half, a three-quarter shape and finally becomes full, though at full phase it is virtually behind the Sun and is out of view. After full it goes through its changes in the reverse order; three-quarter, half, waning crescent and back to new. A complete cycle takes several months.

At its most brilliant, Venus is a crescent. Any small telescope will show the shape, and so will good binoculars, but can the crescent phase be seen with the naked eye?

There is considerable evidence that it can. One needs very keen sight (much keener than mine, even when I have my monocle fixed firmly in position), but I have come across several people who can make out the crescent without too much difficulty. We decided to carry out an experiment, and when Venus was excellently placed I devoted a whole programme to it.

I showed a photograph of Venus as a crescent — one that I had myself taken from my observatory, earlier in the week — and asked viewers to send me drawings of the phase if they could genuinely see it. I stressed the danger of 'wishful

▼ *Crescent Venus. Unfairly, I showed it with the horns or cusps pointing right — the telescopic view.*

◀ *Orbits of Venus and the Earth, showing conjunctions and elongations.*

◀ *The tracks of the last two and next two transits of Venus across the disc of the sun. The dots show the approximate size of Venus when in transit.*

thinking', and asked everyone to take particular care. I added that in the next programme I would show a selection of drawings made by viewers who had been successful.

I must admit that I had not been entirely honest. The picture I showed on the screen was the telescopic view, with south at the top and north at the bottom. All normal telescopes give an upside-down image, though for telescopes used for nonastronomical purposes, such as looking at birds, bathing beauties and ships out to sea, extra lenses are included to turn the image the right way up again. But having an inverted image does not in the least matter to an astronomer, who wants to collect as much light as possible. Since a ray of light is slightly weakened every time it passes through a chunk of glass, the correcting lenses are simply left out.

Therefore, in my screen picture the crescent Venus was shown with the 'horns' pointing right. We waited eagerly for the results.

As before, replies came in thick and fast, and I had a grand total of over four hundred drawings. All except four showed the horns pointing right — the telescopic view! The remaining four viewers were distinctly baffled. 'I could see that Venus was a crescent,' wrote one man, 'but it seemed to be the wrong way round. Are you sure you didn't make a mistake during the programme?' Of course, the truth was that the four wrong-way sketches were the only genuine sightings; the rest were due to imagination, which just shows that it is only too easy to 'see' what one expects to see. The experiment may not have told us much astronomically, but psychologically it was, I think, of some value.

The other Venus programme — rather later, in 1969 — was of a different type, and I mention it here because it involved my playing a harpsichord, something that I had never done before and have never done since.

Look back at the diagram, and you will see that when Venus is new it is practically between the Earth and the Sun. If the lining-up is exact, then of course Venus will be seen as a black disc against the Sun's brilliant face; this is what is called a transit. It does not happen every time Venus is new, because the planet's orbit is slightly tilted with respect to ours, and at most times of 'new Venus' the planet passes unseen either slightly above or slightly below the Sun in the sky. Everything has to be just right, and this happens only rarely. Transits occur in pairs, separated by eight years, after which there are no more for over a century. Thus there were transits in 1631, 1639, 1761, 1769, 1874 and 1882; the next will be in 2004 and 2012.

En passant, I am virtually sure that there is nobody now living who can remember a transit of Venus. Assuming that one's memory goes back to the age of three,[1] an observer still

---

[1] *My own first recollection is of the General Strike of 1926. I distinctly remember my parents driving me into Bognor to buy me a new pair of shoes, since Bognor, as a non-Union town, kept open throughout. It hadn't then become Bognor Regis.*

alive today must have reached the advanced age of a hundred and eight. If I am wrong, and there is such a person around, I would be most grateful if he (or she) would let me know, as I would love to invite him to join me in a programme before it is too late!

Stories about transits are legion. There was the famous French astronomer Legentil, who went to India in 1761 to study the transit — which was important at the time, because for reasons which need not concern us here the phenomenon provided a good way of measuring the planet's distance from Earth, which would in turn lead to an estimate of the distance between the Earth and the Sun. Unhappily, the Seven Years' War was raging (England and France were almost always at each other's throats during that period), and Legentil arrived too late. Rather than risk another delay, he elected to stay where he was and observe the 1769 transit instead. Predictably, the days before and after the transit were brilliantly clear, but the actual phenomenon was hidden by clouds, and Legentil, realizing that it was rather too long to wait for the next transit (that of 1874) packed up to go home. Twice he was shipwrecked, and finally reached Paris to find that he had been presumed dead, so that his heirs were preparing to distribute his property. One imagines that his enthusiasm for transits was somewhat dampened.

But, you may ask, why rake all this up in 1969?

The answer was that it was the 200th anniversary of the 1769 transit, which had been widely observed even though Legentil had missed it. Captain Cook's voyage to the South Seas was not originally intended to be one of discovery; his task was to take a team of astronomers to Tahiti, where the transit was expected to be (and indeed was) clearly seen. On the way home, Cook discovered Australia. This was an anniversary which we could hardly ignore.

My initial suggestion was to go to Tahiti, where the site of Cook's expedition is still called Point Venus. Alas, the BBC showed a signal lack of enthusiasm — they pointed out that it would cost a good deal of money; they tend to think that way on such occasions — and we had to settle for Hoole, in Cheshire, instead. Without claiming for a moment that Hoole is as glamorous as Tahiti, it was relevant enough, because it was from here that Jeremiah Horrocks, a local curate, had been the first to record a transit of Venus. The date had been 1639.

Horrocks had worked things out for himself, because he was an excellent mathematician, and would certainly have made his mark in the scientific world had he not died so young. He had a small telescope, and set it up in the garden of Carr House, which still stands. He began watching the Sun early, in case his

calculations had been in error, but unfortunately it was a Sunday, and he was called away to attend to his clerical duties, so that he was able to see only the last stages of the transit, just before sunset. One other observer also managed a glimpse: William Crabtree, in Liverpool, whom Horrocks had alerted.

To Carr House we repaired, complete with cameras. At that stage the house had been turned into a doll museum, and to be candid I found it rather sinister; there were dolls of all sorts, shapes and sizes, staring down at us from shelves, mantelpieces and cupboards as though wondering what on earth we were trying to do. I half expected them to start dancing around, in the manner of the dolls in Rossini/Respighi's *Fantastic Toyshop*. They didn't — they merely sat there, stuffed and mute — and we prepared for our broadcast. We had already set the scene, and had taken shots of the 'Horrocks' stained-glass windows in the local church, which are worth seeing if you ever happen to go there, but there was not much else of historical relevance.

As I have said earlier, the opening theme music for *The Sky at Night* has always been Sibelius's 'At the Castle Gate'. For years we used an old German 78-rpm recording which is still, in my view, one of the finest renderings I have heard (when we finally abandoned it the BBC kindly presented me with the record, which I still have). A quarter of an hour before transmission was due, we looked around for it.

It wasn't there.

What to do? We were too far away from any local shop to buy a replacement, and in any case it was then nearly eleven o'clock in the evening. We couldn't get it relayed via the studio in Lime Grove, because all members of the record department had long since gone home to bed. We thought furiously. Then we had an idea. Was there a piano around?

I am a very amateur musician; the only thing I am prepared to play in public is the xylophone, and this would hardly have been appropriate even if there had been a xylophone handy. A piano would have been one possibility, but there wasn't a piano either. All we could find was an ancient harpsichord, which looked as though it dated from about the time of Henry the Eighth and had not been played since.

I sat down, and tried it out. It wheezed somewhat. I had never in my life played 'At the Castle Gate', but I do have a good ear, and I thought that I could just about manage it. Well — nothing ventured, nothing gained. Having made sure that most of the notes worked, I had a quick run through; there was no time for more. The cameras were somehow turned towards the harpsichord, and we began transmission.

Whether or not Sibelius turned in his grave I do not know. In his place, I am sure I would have done. But at least it was recognizable, and it provided another 'first' for the programme, albeit an unintentional one.

I doubt if the programme itself was of special note; but, remember, another transit of Venus is coming up in less than two decades hence. If I am still broadcasting, I will most certainly do my best to show it, but I promise that on that occasion I won't play the harpsichord. Once is enough.

▼ *The stained-glass window in Hoole Church, honouring the onetime curate there, Jeremiah Horrocks.*

9
Siberian Interlude

In June 1969 I bade farewell to the Armagh Planetarium; as I have said, flying to and from England had become too much of a problem,[1] quite apart from other factors. It took some time to transfer everything (including cat) back to Sussex, but before long I was on my travels again, this time to Siberia.

Most people think of Siberia as a land of fur-capped peasants, salt-mines, tundra and reindeer, seared by Arctic winds and permanently at sub-zero temperatures. This may be true of the Asiatic part of it — not having been there, I don't know — but the European side of it is less forbidding, and it was from here, on 22 September, that another total solar eclipse was due. Flushed with our earlier success, we laid our plans, only to find that taking television equipment across the Siberian border was impossible. Not that the Russians were unhelpful; they weren't, but the purely practical obstacles defeated us. Therefore it was agreed that I should go on my own, take what pictures I could, and give a first-hand report when I came back.

As a piece of personal research, I proposed to carry out a hunt for comets. These bizarre members of the Sun's family have been known to creep up on us unawares, and if they approach from behind the Sun we can easily overlook them. When the eclipse becomes total the surrounding sky darkens enough for any errant comets to show up, as had happened in 1882, when a photograph showed not only the corona but also a bright comet, a few degrees from the Sun's edge, which had never been seen before and was never seen again. Of course, it was a 'long shot', but I would have loved to have discovered a new comet during the course of a *Sky at Night* expedition.

Yurgamysh, the site chosen by the Russians for all the various expeditions, is not far inside the Siberian border, and quite a number of enthusiasts, both amateur and professional, were scheduled to converge there. The nearest towns you are likely to find on an ordinary map are Kurgan and Sverdlovsk. From Keele University came an old friend, Dr Ron Maddison; from Holland, Professor Houtgast; there were Swedes, Danes, Americans, Germans — in fact, representatives from many nations. I found out that the weather was unlikely to be wildly hot or intensely cold, because that part of Siberia was going through its autumn, which lasts for about a week.

Then came the first hitch. The Soviet authorities became

---

[1]*To say that the airlines were entirely dependable would be an overstatement. Once we were flying by BEA across the Irish Sea, after a lengthy delay, when the pilot came over with an announcement: 'Ladies and gentlemen, we apologize for the late departure from Belfast. One of the engines wouldn't start.' I have always remembered this as a superb exercise in public relations.*

very difficult about granting me a visa. Russia itself was fine — after all, I was (and still am) an Honorary Member of the Astronomical Society of the USSR, thanks to my Moon-mapping activities — but Siberia came under a different set of rules and regulations, and, believe me, our own charming Civil Service has nothing on that of Soviet Russia. Sir Humphrey Appleby would be in his element there.

Once this became known, the Press questioned me closely, but I said little except that the Russians were fully entitled to say who they do or do not want to visit them. If I were regarded as a filthy Western capitalist warmonger, who had made many ideological mistakes and had deviated strongly from the Socialist doctrines of Karl Marx and V.I. Lenin, who was I to argue? I cast my mind back to my first visit to Moscow, in 1959, when I had almost caused an international incident by parking my fur hatski on a bust which turned out to be that of Lenin; but I hardly thought that this could be the cause of the problem. Anyway, I asked Ron Maddison to photograph the eclipse for me, and remained at home.

Four days before the eclipse I had a call from the Royal Society. Urgent messages had come through from the USSR Academy of Sciences in Moscow. I was welcome in Siberia after all . . . . Could I catch the flight from Heathrow at noon on the next day, having first been to the Soviet Embassy to collect the visa waiting for me?

It was all rather a rush. My car was being repaired; there were no reliable trains to London, because as usual British Rail had been caught completely off its guard by the onset of autumn, and the roads were little better, because many of them were flooded. Somehow I got to London by breakfast-time, picked up my visa, prevailed upon the BBC to provide some travellers' cheques, and struggled to the airport. By noon I was on an Aeroflot flight to Moscow.

End of the problem? Not so. My visa turned out to be for Moscow only. Luckily, I managed to contact Dr Khurikov, of the Soviet Academy, as soon as I landed, and he explained that a Siberian visa would have to be rushed through. Normally, to rush anything through the Russian Civil Service takes about six months. Dr Khurikov, to his eternal credit, managed it in about six hours, and again entrusting myself to Aeroflot, I travelled onward to Kurgan, where I joined up with some German scientists before setting off for the site at Yurgamysh. There was one odd incident in the Kurgan hotel. I wanted to contact Dr Maddison, who was presumably already on the eclipse site; the Russians misunderstood me — was I ill, and if so should they call a surgeon? Before I knew what was happening, the hospital authorities were on my trail. I had asked for Dr

Maddison; they thought I wanted a doctor of *medicine* . . . .

Having sorted that one out, we went on a 2½ hour drive to Yurgamysh, which consists entirely of a children's summer camp which had been evacuated a few days earlier because of the impending onset of winter. The expeditions were set up in a large field, and as I approached I could see plenty of activity. In the hurry of departure I had had no time to pack more than a small suitcase, which I was carrying, and which was crammed with cameras to the exclusion of almost everything else; I did not even have an overcoat, and as I walked across to the site, saying, 'Have I come to the right place?' there was a good deal of ribald laughter.

The equipment was quite elaborate. The Russians meant to make studies of the sky brightness and the structure of the corona; the Americans were concentrating upon photographic measurements of the chromosphere; the Italians, the Swedes and the Swiss were particularly interested in a phenomenon called the flash spectrum, which is of great importance but need not concern us here. Ron Maddison's goal was large-scale photography. Then, as I went around, I came across the famous Dutch astronomer Dr Houtgast, whose equipment seemed to consist entirely of a large armchair. Knowing that he was one of the world's leading eclipse experts, I could not resist stopping to ask what he meant to do.

He gave me a wise smile. 'I have been to many eclipses,' he said in his accented English. 'I have made many observations. Never have I had time to watch an eclipse and enjoy myself. So this time — I do absolutely nozzings!'

Neither did he. While everyone else was working flat out during the fleeting seconds of totality, Dr Houtgast simply laid back in his armchair and watched. I am sure that he had the

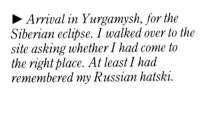

► *Arrival in Yurgamysh, for the Siberian eclipse. I walked over to the site asking whether I had come to the right place. At least I had remembered my Russian hatski.*

right attitude of mind.

Conditions proved to be quite good. There was no cloud trouble; the corona was spectacular, and so were the prominences. I swept for comets, without success, but I have to admit that for part of the time I followed Dr Houtgast's example and merely stared. We had expected 43 seconds of totality, but actually we had only 37, because the Sun began to reappear early through a valley in the Moon's limb. The light flooded back over the Siberian field, and the sensation of unreality — so evident before totality — had passed.

I think we all felt elated. The experiments had worked well, and it had been worth coming so far across the world.

I do have one other vivid memory of that trip. The Russians had provided a banquet in the restaurant of the children's camp, and had invited all the astronomers, plus the entire permanent population of Yurgamysh (all ten of them). Vodka flowed freely; there were speeches, including one from Dr Gnevyshev, leader of the Soviet team; and then brief statements from the various national parties. When my turn came I stood up and said how glad we had all been to be there. 'It's really great,' I said. 'All of us are here in friendship, concerned entirely with the Sun. If only the politicians could see us now!' At which a leading Soviet astronomer rose to his feet, brandished a glass of vodka, and thundered, 'Ah! the politicians! We do not want these gentlemen here!'

He didn't actually say 'gentlemen' — the word he used was much more basic — but, like Dr Houtgast, he had the right idea. I couldn't have put it better myself.

▲ *The total eclipse, as seen from Yurgamysh. The corona was quite spectacular.*

10
Report from the Moon

◄ *Launch of Apollo 8, on 21 December 1968. I did not see it except on television; I was preparing to commentate from Alexandra Palace.*

▲ *Full-scale model of the Apollo 11 Lunar Module, as it was shown at Houston in July 1969 just before the actual flight. I am in the foreground to give a size comparison.*

▲ Colonel Edwin Aldrin at
Tranquillity Base, Apollo 11, July
1969, with part of the equipment left
on the Moon. The Lunar Module is
in the background. I was actually
'on the air' for the whole of the
Moon-walk by Armstrong and
Aldrin.

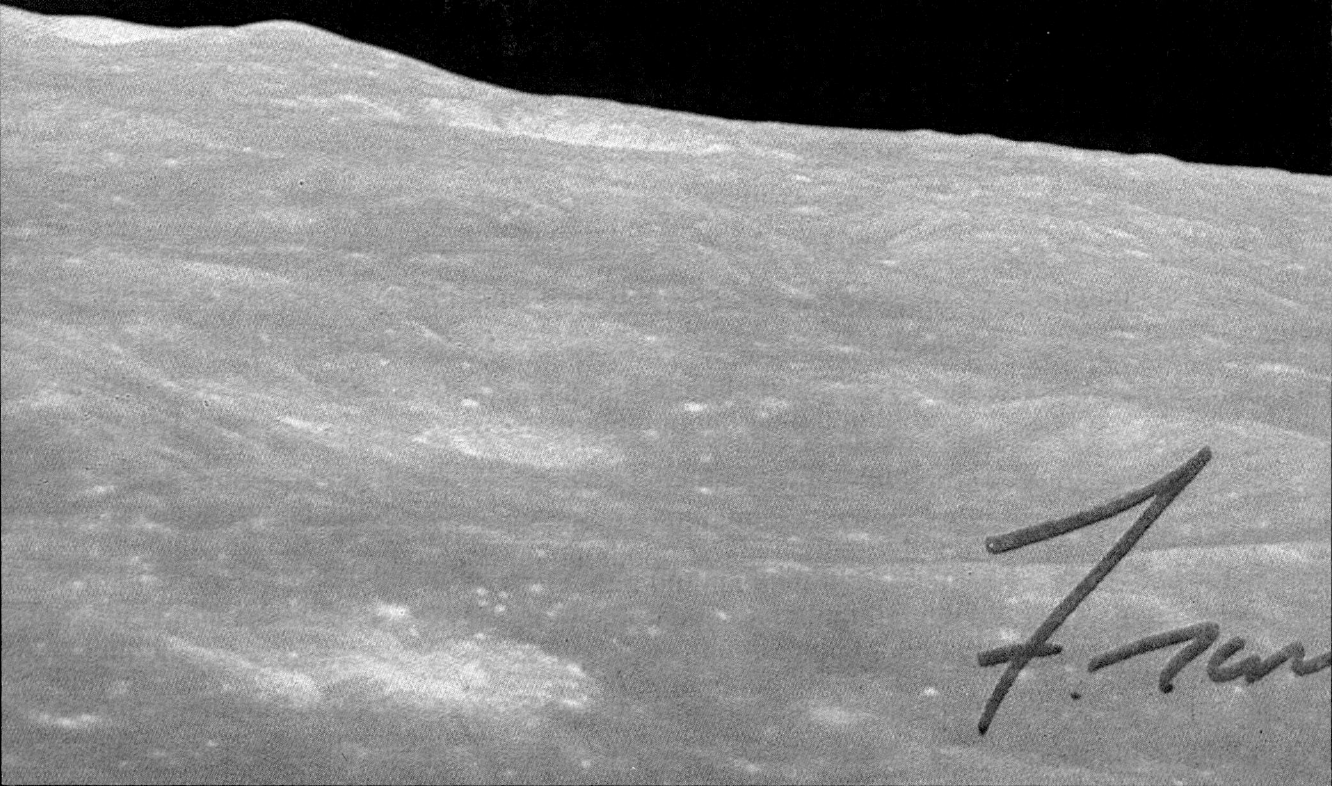

◀ (previous page) *View of the Moon from Apollo 8; Christmas 1968. This is a photograph of the picture given to me by Colonel Frank Borman.*

◀ *Columbia, from Eagle. The command module of Apollo 11, photographed from the lunar module during the lunar-landing mission.*

▶ *On the Moon. Edwin Aldrin at Tranquillity Base, with one of the experiments of the ALSEP (Apollo Lunar Surface Experimental Package).*

▼ *With the Apollo 17 Command Module, which was then (1979) on show at Houston. It is sobering to reflect that this vehicle has been to the Moon and back.*

During the mid-1960s we had to face a new situation in *The Sky at Night*; we went into colour. Of course, this had many advantages, but it had its problems too. One had to be careful what to wear; the early colour cameras didn't like bright white or inky black, for example, so that white shirts were banned. Also, many viewers were restricted to black-and-white receivers. At least I did not commit the gaffe perpetrated later by a snooker commentator, who said: 'He's going for the yellow ball. For those of you who haven't got colour sets, the yellow ball is about two inches to the left of the green.'[1]

Meanwhile, the Moon was coming very much to the fore, mainly because of President Kennedy's avowed intention of seeing an American land there before 1970. I spent some time at the Lowell Observatory in Arizona, busy on official lunar cartography, but of course we devoted regular *Sky at Night* programmes to it, two of which were particularly memorable so far as I was concerned.

The first was in January 1966. Following the fiasco with Luna 4 (by that time the generic term 'Lunik' had been replaced by 'Luna') the Russians had made several more abortive attempts to soft-land automatic probes, and it was clear that success could not be long delayed. This was of fundamental importance, because at that time nobody was quite confident about the strength of the lunar surface. According to one theory, championed by Dr Thomas Gold, the dark 'seas' at least were likely to be filled with soft dust, so that, in Gold's words, 'any spacecraft landing there will simply sink into the dust with all its gear'. After a long and dangerous journey through space, this would be most discouraging, but most lunar observers were sceptical, because the theory did not seem to fit the facts. In my view, at least, the rocks were probably more than firm enough to bear the weight of a spacecraft, particularly since an object on the Moon weighs only one-sixth as much as it does on Earth.

We decided to build a model of a lunar crater, and then illuminate it from the side, so that we could show the changing shadow effects during the progress of a lunar day (which, of course, is almost fourteen times as long as ours, because the Moon is such a slow spinner). The Effects Department built various plaster craters, but unfortunately they looked like plaster. Finally I suggested using sand. This was much better, and I carefully built up a crater looking truly realistic.

When we rehearsed the programme, shortly before transmission, there were problems in raising and lowering the sidelights, so it was decided to tilt the sand-tray upon which the crater had been constructed. This was fine — until we tilted it

---

[1] *I can assure you that this is true. I was watching at the time.*

too far, when suddenly and quite devastatingly the whole mass of sand slid off the tray on to the studio floor. I had about five minutes in which to rebuild it!

On 1 February 1966 the Russian vehicle Luna 9 touched down in the lunar Ocean of Storms, and showed no inclination whatever to sink out of sight. This was one of the occasions when we mounted a *Sky at Night* 'special', and everything went according to plan. Next came the American Surveyors, which also made controlled landings, and these were accompanied by the five Orbiters, which went round and round the Moon, sending back close-range pictures of the entire surface — the far side as well as the familiar hemisphere. Within a year (August 1966 to August 1967) all Earth-drawn maps of the Moon, including mine, became obsolete. One formation which showed up well was the Mare Orientale, or Eastern Sea, in which I had a fatherly interest because years earlier I had discovered it myself, and had even suggested its name. It lies on the extreme edge of the Moon's Earth-turned hemisphere, and only part of it is visible from here even under ideal conditions. The Orbiters showed it to be a vast, multi-ringed structure, far more important than I had had any reason to expect. The name seems odd now, because by a 1965 edict of the International Astronomical Union, the controlling body of world astronomy, 'east' and 'west' on the Moon were officially reversed, so that as seen from Earth my *Eastern* Sea is now on the *western* limb . . .

All this was building up towards the Apollo missions. In 1968 came the first manned flight round the Moon, with Apollo 8. On 21 December Colonel Frank Borman, Captain James Lovell and Major William Anders blasted off from Cape Canaveral, and by Christmas Eve they were nearing their target. Their first task was to fire the spacecraft's rockets and put themselves into a closed path round the Moon. This had to be done when they were actually *behind* the Moon, so that they were then completely out of touch. Their radio signals could not reach us, and they were cut off from all mankind.

At that time all the news broadcasts were transmitted not from Lime Grove, but from Alexandra Palace, near Wood Green. It was here that I was stationed, on my own apart from the BBC technicians; everyone else had gone home. I was on the air live as the critical moment approached, and I can more or less remember my exact words:

'The Apollo 8 astronauts have passed behind the Moon, and by now they will have fired their on-board rockets, with the aim of putting themselves into lunar orbit. But remember, there is only one chance. If all goes well, we will hear their signals in less than a minute from now. If the rockets have misfired, there is a chance that they will have hurled themselves into the wrong orbit, in which case they will be in the utmost danger — and of course there is always the dread possibility that we will not hear them at all, in which case we may never know what happened. All we can do is to wait. I will say no more; listen out for the signals in less than twenty seconds. This is one of the great moments in human history.'

And the BBC switched over to *Jackanory*.

I did get back on the air a few minutes later, by which time, thankfully, the Apollo 8 signals had come through right on schedule. But it was a episode which must surely remain unique in the story of broadcasting!

Apollo 9, next in the series, was an Earth orbiter designed to test out the lunar module. Apollo 10 was another circumlunar flight, and then, in July 1969, came Apollo 11, carrying Neil Armstrong, Edwin Aldrin and Michael Collins. I remained as one of the two regular commentators (James Burke was the other), and we were able to give full coverage until the Apollo missions ended in December 1972.

My own lunar mapping lay in the past, but at least I knew many of the astronauts, because I had met them at various NASA conferences in my rôle as an astonomer. I also felt that in a way I rather spanned the ages. I knew Yuri Gagarin, the first man in space; I knew Wernher von Braun, the rocket pioneer; I still know Neil Armstrong, the first man on the Moon, and I once met Orville Wright, the first man to fly in a heavier-than-air machine. This does not make me quite so ancient as might be thought, because Orville Wright did not die until the late 1940s, and I had had my one meeting with him when I was myself an air cadet in the early months of the war. All the same, it does show how quickly things have moved. Remember, as late as 1903 one of America's leading scientists, Professor Simon Newcomb, was still maintaining no aeroplane could take off without being pulled along by swarms of little birds.

As the Apollo missions progressed, so the BBC coverage became more and more elaborate. The programmes were special ones, not part of the *Sky at Night* series, so that they do not really belong to this book, but I maintain that they showed the truth of what I call Moore's Law: 'The efficiency and interest of any television programme varies in inverse ratio to the numbers of producers and directors involved.' For Apollos 8 to 11 we had one producer and two commentators. By the end of Apollo 17 we had at least ten producers and swarms of commentators, though James and I still acted as the link men. Of course, some of our studio guests were eminent scientists as well as being first-class broadcasters, and I have particular memories of Dr Stuart Agrell and Professor Geoffrey Eglinton, the lunar geologists, who made splendid contributions. They usually occupied one corner of Studio 7 in Television Centre, and I am sure they will not mind my recalling that we used to call their contributions the Ag and Egg Show!

Apollo 11 was launched on 16 July 1969. A week earlier the Russians had dispatched their unmanned Luna 15, with the aim of landing it in the Sea of Crises and bringing back samples of Moon-rock (something which had not been done before, though it has been achieved twice since). Nobody was sure whether or not Luna 15 was an attempt to upstage Apollo. I was convinced that it wasn't, but all the same the BBC asked me to fly to Moscow and see what I could find out.

This was quite a challenge, because my knowledge of the Russian language is nil, and when I arrived I found that the resident BBC staff could not be of much help. Then I had a stroke of luck. An astronomical conference was being held at Moscow University, and as a member of the International Astronomical Union I was invited. I then managed to collect three English-speaking Soviet scientists, a camera crew and a sound recordist on the University steps at the same time, and proudly returned to London with a film which was shown that night. I am convinced that the Russians were merely continuing with their own missions in their own way; actually Luna 15 failed, as it crash-landed on 21 July and sent back no useful data, but by then, naturally, all the world's attention was concentrated upon Apollo 11.

One of our minor problems was air-conditioning. Studio 7 in Television Centre is large, but the weather during that week was sweltering hot, and the lights raised the temperature to a positively Venusian level. Unfortunately, we had a large globe of the Moon suspended in a prominent position, and every time we switched on the air-conditioning the globe danced about in a most bizarre manner, so we had to perspire and make the best of it.

On the night of the landing itself, I was broadcasting continuously for over ten hours, and I will not forget it. One of the main weaknesses of the Apollo project was the lack of any provision for rescue, so that if the capsule made a faulty landing, or if the single ascent engine of the lunar module failed to work first time, the astronauts would have been doomed. As Neil Armstrong and Buzz Aldrin were descending in the *Eagle*, Apollo 11's lunar module, I could not help thinking 'Suppose we've all been wrong! Suppose the ground is unsafe, after all . . .' When I heard Neil's voice coming through — 'The *Eagle* has landed' — I felt a tremendous surge of relief — shared, I have no doubt, by all the millions of people who were viewing or listening. Frankly, I do not remember just what I said; I hope it was appropriate.

We stayed on transmission for Neil's 'one small step' on to the Sea of Tranquillity, and I did not come off the air until well after breakfast-time on the following morning. By then I was flagging, but mercifully Joan Marsden, the floor manager (of whom more anon), presented me with what looked superficially like a cup of coffee, but which was, I think, almost neat brandy. Anyway, it did the trick.

▼ *In the studio! Geoffrey Pardoe, the rocket expert (to my right) and James Burke. Joan Marsden ('Mother') carries out an emergency adjustment to her shoe, or something. This was taken in 1969, during the Apollo 11 coverage.*

Each Apollo mission had its own characteristics. With No. 12, in November 1969, the lunar camera was put out of action almost at once because it was accidentally pointed at the Sun, so that we had to carry out our commentaries more or less 'blind'. Apollo 13 was the most tense, for obvious reasons. I had gone home after a broadcast when, at 3 a.m., I was telephoned with the news that there had been an explosion on board the spacecraft; I drove back to Shepherd's Bush at breakneck speed, and stayed there, broadcasting periodically, until the crisis was over. At one point I was able to talk (privately) to the then Controller of NASA, and asked him whether the chances of rescue were good. 'Yes,' he replied, 'if nothing else goes wrong.' Mercifully it didn't, and for a brief period it seemed as though the world had united, with the usual political bickerings and squabblings put temporarily into cold storage.

The last Apollos, Nos. 14 to 17, were the most scientifically oriented. I was actually in Mission Control for the last of them; previously the BBC policy — of which I thoroughly approved — had been to leave me in London while the rest of the team went to the States, so that I could hold the fort in case of any breakdown in communications.

Apollo 17 was a night launch, and was all the more spectacular for that. What I remember most is the intense glare from the departing rocket, and the realization that there were three men in the midst of it. There was additionally what I can only call a 'wall of sound', deafening even though we were several miles from the site itself. I was also in Mission Control when Dr Schmitt, the geologist-astronaut, called out that he had found 'orange soil — crazy!' Momentarily we thought that it might indicate recent volcanic activity on the Moon, but in the end it proved to be due to tiny orange-coloured particles several thousands of millions of years old.

Though the Apollo programmes were not in the official *Sky at Night*, I cannot pass over two of our later broadcasts. One went out in November 1970, and our guest was none other than Neil Armstrong. We were not in Television Centre, but in the foyer of a London hotel, where Neil was scheduled to appear first on one of the BBC's prestigious news programmes and then with me. During the first broadcast he was bombarded with all the usual loaded questions: 'Does it justify the cost?' 'What about feeding the starving millions?' 'Can you really claim that it has been worth while?' and so on. He fended these tactfully, but as soon as he crossed the floor to join me for *The Sky at Night* he sank into a chair and said thankfully: 'Now we can talk some science.' We did.

Then there was the Lunar Landing Simulator . . . This was more or less on the lines of an RAF Link trainer, suitably

modified, so that the 'astronaut' had to work everything out, conserving his fuel until he was ready to touch down at zero velocity. We were joined by one of the Moon-men (for once I won't give his name!) and we tried it out. As an ex-pilot, though a very poor one, I went first, and by more luck than judgment I made a safe landing. Then came the astronaut. At the end of his approach the simulator flashed a sign: THERE WERE NO SURVIVORS: LUCKY IT WAS ONLY A PRACTICE. As he had actually done it on the real Moon and I hadn't, my faith in the simulator was somewhat shattered.

Much later, in 1982, I talked in Houston to Commander Eugene Cernan, commander of Apollo 17 and the last man (so far) to walk on the Moon. We intended to record a two-minute interview for the *Sky at Night* 25th anniversary, but as soon as we began I knew that we had something really special. I glanced at Pieter Morpurgo, who was directing as well as producing, and he gave a quick nod, so we went on for twenty minutes. It made a complete programme, and all we had to do was to top and tail it.

On the whole, our pre-Apollo ideas about the Moon were not

▲ *Neil Armstrong. Neil and I attended a seminar together in Glasgow. The first man on the Moon seems pleased to be back on mother Earth.*

so very wide of the mark. There is no atmosphere; there is no life there, and never has been; the seas were never water-filled, though they were once oceans of lava. Nothing moves; the flags planted by the Apollo astronauts do not flutter, and will remain as they are until someone collects them. So too will the Lunar Rovers or Moon-cars used by the last three expeditions. They remain on the lunar surface, and there is nothing to damage them, so that they must still be fully functional. In the future, a new Moon-man will go up to them, put in new batteries and drive them off to a museum.

When that will be I do not know; sadly, it depends more upon politics and finance than upon science or logic. But to quote Neil Armstrong, 'in some ways the Moon is more hospitable than the Antarctic. There are no storms, no snow, no high winds, no unpredictable weather; as for the gravity — well, the Moon's a very pleasant place to work in; better than the Earth, I think.'

He certainly ought to know. Sadly, I have no hope of going into space, particularly as I would need a very powerful launcher, but I am sure that a successor of mine will present a *Sky at Night* from the lunar surface. If this happens while I am still alive, I will take care to make a detailed video.

◀ *The first piece of Moon rock. It was carried out in a sealed compartment, because for Apollo 11 all samples were quarantined. I was there (outside the sealed compartment, I hasten to add).*

11
The Red Dog-Star

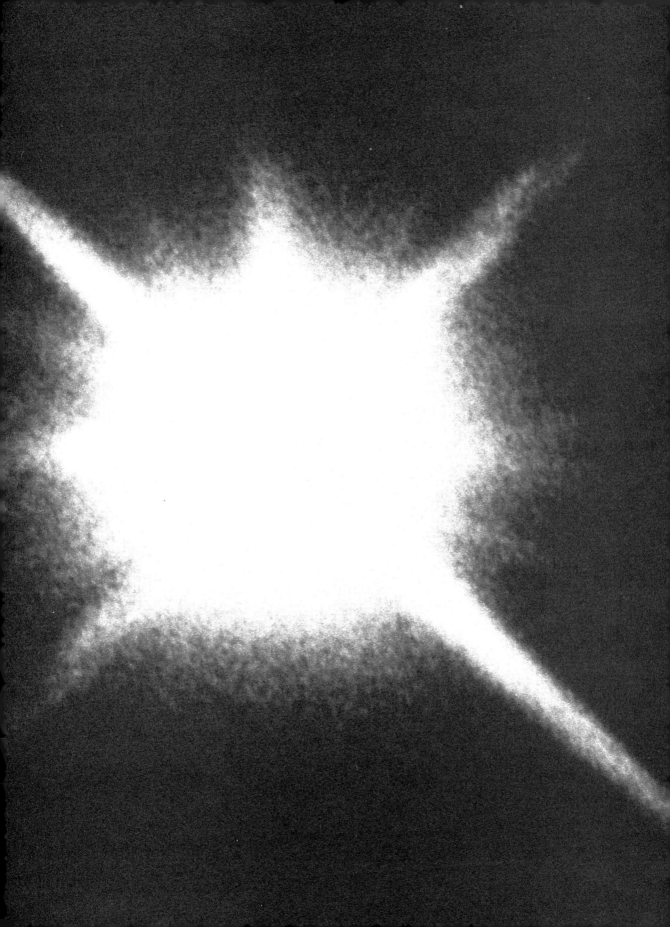

In many ways I regret the passing of live television for programmes such as ours. Not that it makes any difference to the way we go about things; it doesn't, but I suppose that it removes a certain amount of urgency, because if anything goes wrong you can always reshoot. As soon as recordings became equal in quality to direct transmissions we began to use them. Of course, there are some programmes which have to remain live; if, for example, you are dealing with a solar eclipse lasting for a few seconds, you cannot simply call out 'Take Two!' on the grounds that there is a hair in the camera lens or that the presenter has swallowed a fly. (I did once swallow a large fly during an early broadcast, when I had just opened my mouth to make some world-shattering pronouncement. The producer — still Paul Johnstone in that era — said that he saw a look of glazed horror come into my eyes, after which I gave a strangled gulp and went on. My mother later summed it up beautifully: 'Yes, dear — it was nasty for you, but so much worse for the fly.' I suppose she was right.)

With the *Sky at Night*, the change came around 1970. We have to record near the time of transmission, as otherwise we are apt to be caught out by the rush of events, since by Spode's Law the appearance of a bright comet or new star always occurs

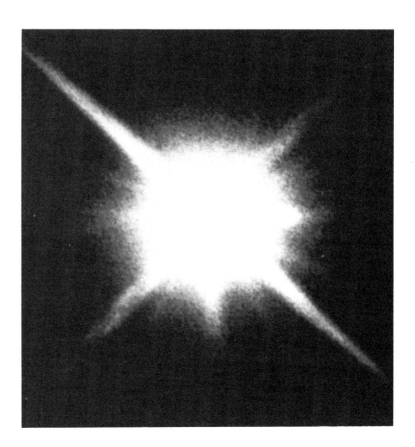

▶ *Sirius B. The tiny 'Pup' close to the brilliant primary. The spikes from Sirius itself are, of course, purely photographic effects.*

just before we are due on the air. But it also means that we can be somewhat more elaborate than of yore.

Moreover, *The Sky at Night* always comes on late at night, so that live broadcasts would mean keeping the camera crews up to what are termed unsociable hours. This is quite in order for astronomers, who are meant to be night owls, but I did once make an official protest when we finally appeared on the screen well after midnight following a half-hour programme in which an admittedly potty poet sat in his garden spouting reams of meaningless verse. In my letter I expressed the hope that *The Sky at Night* had been enjoyed by both the viewers who were still switched on. (Latterly, I am glad to say, we have been given regular early-evening repeats to satisfy the needs of younger enthusiasts who had complained bitterly about being sent to bed before we came on the air.)

One of our early recordings provided another chance to involve the audience. It concerned Sirius, the brightest star in the sky, which is the leader of the constellation Canis Major (the Great Dog) and is popularly known as the Dog-Star. I must say a little about Sirius, because otherwise what follows will mean nothing at all; I promise you that I will not delve into abstruse scientific detail.

Sirius is easy to find. It is prominent in the evening sky over Britain all through winter and early spring, and it is so brilliant that you cannot mistake it, though of course it is still outshone by a few of the planets (Venus, Jupiter and Mars at its best). Sirius lies in line with the three stars making up the Belt of Orion, the Hunter. Orion has a characteristic pattern; two of its stars, Betelgeux[1] and Rigel, are very bright and are clearly unlike each other, because Betelgeux is orange-red while Rigel is pure white. The Belt lies in the middle part of the constellation, and from it extends the misty Sword, about which I will have more to say later.

The fact that the stars are of different colours shows that their surfaces are not equally hot. White is hotter than yellow, which is in turn hotter than red, so that the white Rigel has a temperature higher than that of our yellow Sun, while Betelgeux is cooler. Mind you, even Betelgeux is fairly torrid, and if you could put a thermometer on its surface it would register some 3000 degrees Centigrade.

---

[1] *This name can be spelled in various ways, because it comes from the Arabic and one has to depend upon phonetics. I call it 'Bettle-gurz', but Arabic scholars may disagree. Incidentally, the name 'Sirius' comes from the Greek for 'scorching', and should definitely be pronounced 'Sy-rius', though I think most people refer to it as 'Sirri-us'. Not that it really matters except to pronunciation fanatics!*

Now let us come to Sirius, which is a white star 26 times as luminous as our Sun. Its light, whipping along at the rate of 186,000 miles per second, takes 8·6 years to reach us, from which we can work out that the distance of Sirius is roughly 50 million million miles, and no telescope can show it as anything but a dot of light.

Because Sirius is so brilliant, it is the supreme twinkler, and seems to flash various colours. Twinkling or scintillation has nothing to do with the stars themselves, but is due entirely to the Earth's unsteady atmosphere which may be said to shake the starlight around. However, one thing is definite: Sirius is not red, or even orange-red like Betelgeux. It is all the more curious that many of the astronomers of Classical times, some two thousand years ago, compared it with Mars. Ptolemy, the last great astronomer of the ancient world, was quite definite about this, but there is no doubt that by the ninth century Sirius looked much as it does to-day; so can there have been any real alteration?

One man who believed so was the American astronomer Thomas Jefferson Jackson See. He collected all the evidence he could, and in 1927 he published a lengthy paper about it which caused no stir in the scientific world. This may be because See was not the most popular figure of his day — in fact it is not too much to say that his contemporaries hated the sight of him. The general view was aptly summed up by his erstwhile colleague at the Lowell Observatory, A.E. Douglass: 'Personally I have never had such aversion to a man or beast or reptile or anything disgusting as I have had to him. The moment he leaves town will be one of vast and intense relief, and I never want to see him again. If he ever comes back, I will have him kicked out of town.'

(Incidentally, it was See who suggested in 1930 that the planet discovered by Clyde Tombaugh, and now known as Pluto, should be named 'Minerva'. This is why it wasn't.)

The Sirius riddle seemed to be interesting enough to warrant a programme, involving a little original research, but we first had to decide whether the evidence was even reasonably conclusive. Stars do not usually change colour over periods of a few centuries, and Sirius is a completely stable, well-behaved stellar adult. True, it has a tiny companion which is very dim and very dense, but it did not seem that the answer could lie here, and it appeared more likely that we were dealing with an error in observation or interpretation. Yet there was the twinkling to be borne in mind, and I just wondered whether this could provide a clue.

In the programme, I explained the situation and then asked viewers to co-operate. They were invited to look at Sirius on the next dark, clear, moonless night, and then write down their impressions on a postcard. The results were most gratifying. We had over 5000 replies, and they took a great deal of analysing, but in the end the results were:

Bluish or bluish-white:	50 per cent
White:	23 per cent
Flashing all colours:	14 per cent
Greenish or greenish-white:	9 per cent
Yellowish:	2 per cent
Orange:	2 per cent

Nobody saw Sirius as red, and the 'orange' observers told me that they had made their observations when the star was very low over the horizon. So I think that our modest experiment so far as it went, tended to confirm my original view that nothing has changed in historical times. Yet I must quote one letter I had:

'Sirius is a lovely star, and I look at it every evening. It has ten planets going round it, one of which is very like the Earth and has blue seas and lakes. I know, because I have often been there.'

Another effort at audience participation, around the same time, involved counting the number of naked-eye stars in the open cluster of the Pleiades, in Taurus (the Bull). The usual nickname for the cluster is the Seven Sisters; it is very prominent in the evening sky for several months in each year, and makes up a genuine group, not a mere line-of-sight effect. Binoculars show many extra stars in the cluster, and the total membership amounts to several hundreds, but how many can be glimpsed without optical aid? It is said that Eduard Heis, a last-century German astronomer, could count up to nineteen.

We decided to find out. Again we dispatched cards, and again we had a splendid response. The mean number did indeed work out at 7, so that the nickname is justified, but one chart, from an earnest lady in Manchester, claimed that she could count 241 Sisters. Tactful inquiries showed that she had not only listed the stars in the Pleiades, but had also included the whole of Taurus, and had thrown in part of Orion for good measure.

While on the subject of stars in general, I think I must mention another programme of mid-1971. This time we set out to demonstrate the way in which stellar distances are measured.

The stars are immensely remote. Even the closest of them — not counting the Sun — is some 24 million million miles away, and most of the rest are much farther off still. If you represent the Earth-Sun distance by one inch, the nearest star will have to be taken out to over four miles, and obviously the distances are not easy to measure. The first man to do so successfully was the German astronomer Friedrich Bessel, in 1838, using the method known as parallax.

I demonstrated this in the studio by a simple experiment. 'Close one eye,' I said, 'and then hold up a finger at arm's-length, lining it up with your TV screen. Now, without moving your finger or your head, use the other eye. Your finger will no longer be aligned with the screen, because you are seeing it from a slightly different direction; your two eyes are not in the same place. If you measure the amount of angular shift or parallax, and if you also know the distance between your eyes, you can work out the distance of your finger from your face.'

I hope you can follow that, but the diagram ought to help. In the case of a star, we need a much longer baseline, and we use the Earth at its positions on opposite sides of the Sun. Select a relatively nearby star (there are ways of doing this) and measure its position first in January (A), and then in June (B), by which time the Earth has moved over to the far side of its orbit and has provided a baseline of 186,000,000 miles in length. The star will then show a slight but detectable parallax shift against the background of remote objects.

▼ *The parallax principle. The dot represents the finger as viewed by each eye.*

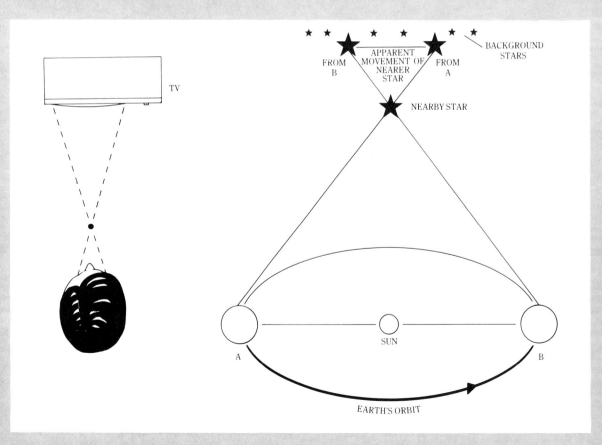

▲ *Parallax . . . with the help of the boys of Holmewood House; the 1st XI took time off from cricket nets to help us.*

To drive the point home, I contacted the headmaster of a famous boys' preparatory school, Holmewood House in Kent, which I knew very well. Could I please borrow the cricket field for a few hours, and also enlist the aid of some members of the First XI? No problem; and to Holmewood House we went.

The idea was to choose one particular boy to represent the nearest star, and then string others out at distances across the field so that we could measure the shift as we moved the camera from one end of our baseline to the other. The opening of the programme was at least novel, because it showed a typical cricket scene with two boys at the wicket and the striker facing up to my bowling. I have played a great deal of club cricket in my life, and still do (I am an enthusiastic Lord's Taverner), and although I have never aspired to be anything more than a village-greener I have collected many wickets with my leg-breaks. My pace is slow-medium, and I have a long, leaping run which a local reporter once likened to a kangaroo doing the barn-dance. After the transmission, I had many comments about it!

For once the weather was kind, and I think that the demonstration was a success. At least I am glad that I did not have to display my skill at batting. Looking back in my diary, I find that my scores that season, up to the start of the programme, had been 0, 0, 0, 0 not out, 0 and 0.

12
Prelude to the Grand Tour

In 1971 Pat Owtram and I paid a visit to the United States. On this occasion we did not have a camera team with us; we were on a reconnaissance, and we were particularly interested in the Grand Tour.

I have already said something about the planet Saturn, with its glorious system of rings. Several programmes have been devoted to it, and in one of these there was a curious mishap. Saturn's upper clouds are very chilly, and I thought that it would be interesting to demonstrate some of the effects of intense cold. One method is to dip an egg into liquid air, leave it there for a brief period and then bring it out and hit it with a hammer; the egg will shatter like a piece of solid glass. At least, it will do so if you freeze it for long enough. On this occasion I didn't. I swung the hammer, and there was a horrible squelching sound; there was egg everywhere — in the camera lens, on the floor, even in the studio manager's eye. Eggs seem to be unlucky so far as the *The Sky at Night* is concerned.

What, then, about the Grand Tour?

This was an ambitious plan to send a spacecraft to four planets in turn: Jupiter, Saturn, Uranus and Neptune. All are gas-giants, but they are not alike, and neither are they as close to each other as might be thought from a diagram. The far

▼ *Saturn's rings.*

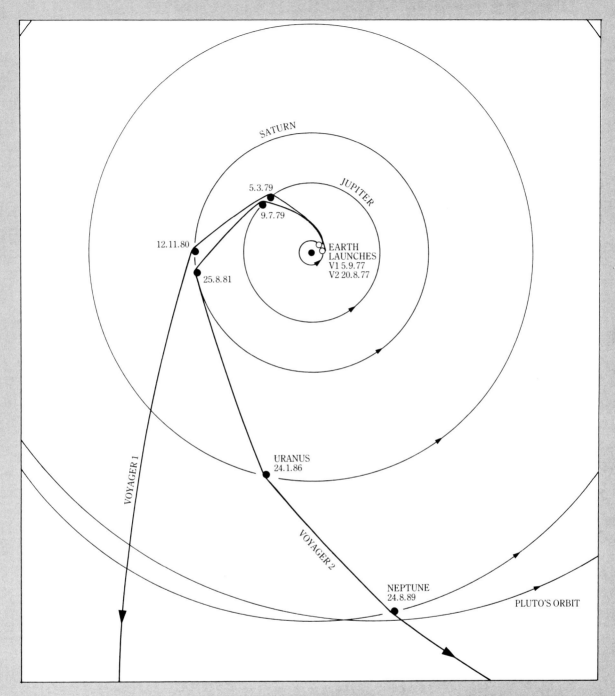

SATURN

JUPITER

5.3.79

9.7.79

EARTH
LAUNCHES
V1 5.9.77
V2 20.8.77

12.11.80

25.8.81

VOYAGER 1

URANUS
24.1.86

VOYAGER 2

NEPTUNE
24.8.89

PLUTO'S ORBIT

▲ *Paths of Voyagers 1 and 2.*

reaches of the Solar System are very spread-out, so that if you could fly straight from the Earth to Neptune, going by the shortest route, the orbit of Uranus would be little more than half-way. I likened this to the opinion of the unwary stay-at-home who looks at a map of Oceania and fondly imagines that one can stand on the coast of Australia and see the white cliffs of New Zealand in the middle distance.

The Grand Tour project was planned well ahead of time, and took advantage of the fact that during the late 1970s the four giants were arranged in a sort of curve (of this, more anon). By the principle of what I irreverently termed interplanetary snooker, the spacecraft could swing past all four in turn. It was important to take advantage of what Nature was offering us, because it would be almost two centuries before the same situation would recur.

NASA was suitably enthusiastic, but the financial controllers were not. Even at that time there were rumblings that too much money was being spent on the exploration of outer space, and the perfectly accurate comment that a planetary probe costs much less than a nuclear submarine made no difference, so that the Grand Tour scheme was steadily whittled down until it was reduced to Jupiter alone. In the event, things worked out unexpectedly well, and the Tour was saved, but we had no inkling of this when we set out on our American trip. Our main idea was to prepare a programme to be devoted to Pioneer 10, the space-vehicle which was due to be launched in March 1972 and was scheduled to by-pass Jupiter in December of the following year.

We went first to the Lowell Observatory in Arizona, set up originally to prove the existence of canals on Mars. This was a welcome and happy return for me; the great 24-inch refractor there is ideal for lunar and planetary work, and I will always hold it in great affection. From Flagstaff we made a quick trip to the Meteor Crater, which is the result of a violet collision over 20,000 years ago between the Earth and a quarter-mile missile from the asteroid belt. We decided that we must take our cameras there, though actually this did not happen until later, and it was 1980 before we devoted a complete programme to the crater. Our next stop was to be the Jet Propulsion Laboratory at Pasadena, in California, headquarters of all the main space missions to the planets. Naturally, we travelled by air, and our journey turned out to be less smooth than we had anticipated.

We used a small airline, which I believe has long since become defunct, and the entire passenger content was no more than a dozen. We took off rather unevenly, and were acutely conscious that we were in for a bumpy ride. This did not bother either of us, but after a while the pilot opened the cabin door and spoke to us. 'We're going to make an unscheduled stop at Farmington. After we took off, part of a wheel was found on the runway. Of course, it wasn't ours — ha, ha! — but we've been asked to land so that it can be checked.'[1]

A pause of perhaps ten minutes. Then: 'Ladies and gentlemen, apparently it was one of our wheels after all. Please fasten your safety-belts securely before we attempt a landing.'

Several passengers turned pale green, but there was very little that anyone could do except wait and see what happened. Looking out of the window, I finally saw Farmington airport, which appeared to consist of a tin hut in the middle of a field. We dropped down, and landed — not gently, but less violently than I had expected, after which the aircraft slewed to a stop and we climbed out, somewhat relieved. We went into the hut, managed to obtain a drink (beer only; this was in Texas) and gazed out across the field. Subsequently we saw a mechanic lying on the ground doing his best to kick a new wheel into position, which inspired us with no confidence at all. We were quite glad to reach Pasadena unscathed.

(Later in the trip we drove through part of Utah, and stopped at a roadside café to refresh ourselves. There were several people around, and one man came up to me with a friendly smile. 'Welcome to our Mormon state,' he said. 'You'll find that this is quite difference from the rest of America; you'll find no swearing, or drinking, or wild women here.' I made the obvious and quite spontaneous reply 'Hardly worth coming, is it?' — after which nobody else would speak to me any more!)

There was no problem about making arrangements for a programme about Pioneer, and I must say at this juncture that all the American astronomers and space-planners have been unfailingly helpful and courteous to us over the years; NASA is publicity-conscious in the best possible way, and I suppose that my status as a member of the IAU in my own right is of some use.

Jupiter is a long way away. Its average distance from the Sun is 483,000,000 miles, and it takes almost twelve years to complete one orbit, though its own 'day' is less than ten hours

---

[1] *I had used the same airline many years before, when I was in the same part of Arizona. On that occasion I was the only passenger, and I went in the co-pilot's seat. At my request we made a slight diversion so that I could photograph Meteor Crater, and subsequently I took over the controls while the pilot took a series of pictures for himself. I found that I was still perfectly happy flying a small turbo-prop aircraft, but I hate to think what the Air Control officials would have said had they found out. It couldn't possibly happen today!*

long. To reach it, the procedure is to launch the space-probe by a massive, compound booster rocket, and then give it an extra thrust which will send it outward. Going by the shortest route is out of the question, because it would mean using fuel all the way, and no vehicle could possibly carry enough. Pioneer would have to travel in what is termed free fall, using the Sun's gravity, meeting Jupiter at a pre-planned point. In a way it is rather like clay-pigeon shooting, but everything has to be almost unbelievably accurate.

There was another potential hazard, too. Between the orbits of Mars and Jupiter circle the minor planets or asteroids, of which several thousands are now known. Most of them are very small; only one (Ceres) is as much as 600 miles in diameter, but when Pioneer was launched nobody was sure whether or not there would be so many dwarf asteroids that the probe would be in grave danger. A collision between Pioneer and a piece of rock the size of, say, an armchair could have only one result. Like so many bogeys of space research, this one has turned out to be unfounded, at least so far as we can tell at the moment, but in 1971 the NASA authorities were very worried about it.

Nothing went wrong. Pioneer survived its journey through the asteroid belt, and on 3 December 1973 it passed within 83,000 miles of Jupiter's cloud-tops, sending back superb pictures as well as a mass of general information. Jupiter turned out to be much as expected, but the magnetic field was remarkably strong, and it was also found that there are zones of lethal radiation which would certainly kill any astronaut foolish enough to venture inside them. Indeed, the instruments of Pioneer 10 were almost saturated, and if the probe had gone any closer the whole equipment would have been put out of action. This is why the path of the next probe, Pioneer 11, was altered so as to make the spacecraft pass quickly over Jupiter's equatorial region, where the radiation is worst.

It was Pioneer 10 which finally gave the *coup de grâce* to Peek's egg theory of the Great Red Spot. Also, it enabled theorists to work out the structure of the planet itself. Apparently there is a solid, very hot core, larger than the Earth and much more massive, surrounded by a tremendously deep liquid layer made up chiefly of hydrogen, outside which comes the gaseous 'atmosphere' ending with the cloud-tops which we can see.

There was another point which we stressed in our eventual programme. Pioneer 10 will never come back. It is moving so quickly that it will escape from the Solar System altogether, and we will finally lose touch with it, though probably not until well into the 1990s. When we can no longer track it it will continue to move between the stars, unseen and unheard, and until it hits some solid object it will go on and on, perhaps passing within reasonable range of the star Altair in about 230,000 years from now. But will anyone else ever find it?

This was something which the NASA authorities had considered. After all, there is no reason to suppose that we are alone in the universe, and other civilizations, living on planets attending other stars, may be far more advanced than we are (which would not be difficult, as you can judge merely by looking at the headlines of the daily papers). Just suppose that an alien race locates Pioneer, and scoops it in for examination. How could they tell from whence it came?

A nice point! So Pioneer carries a plaque, which will, it is hoped, give our unknown aliens the information they need. The plaque is reproduced here. It shows a couple of humanoid figures which have caused some discussion among purists, plus a representation of the Sun and its planets, with a kind of pattern which is intended to give a key to the Sun's position in the Galaxy. Well, I suppose that it is better than nothing, but I must say that if a denizen of Altair C manages to locate us by using the message on the plaque he's a better man than I am, Gunga Din.

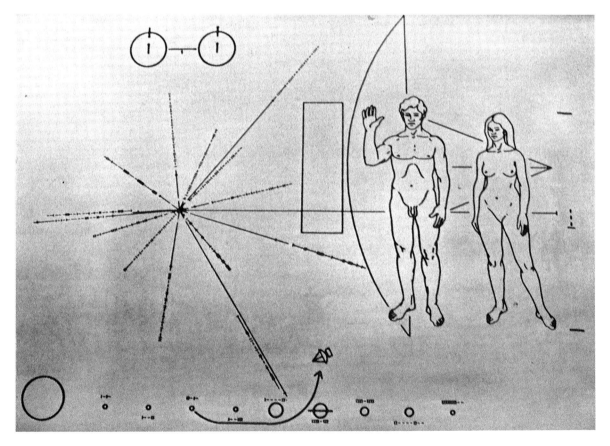

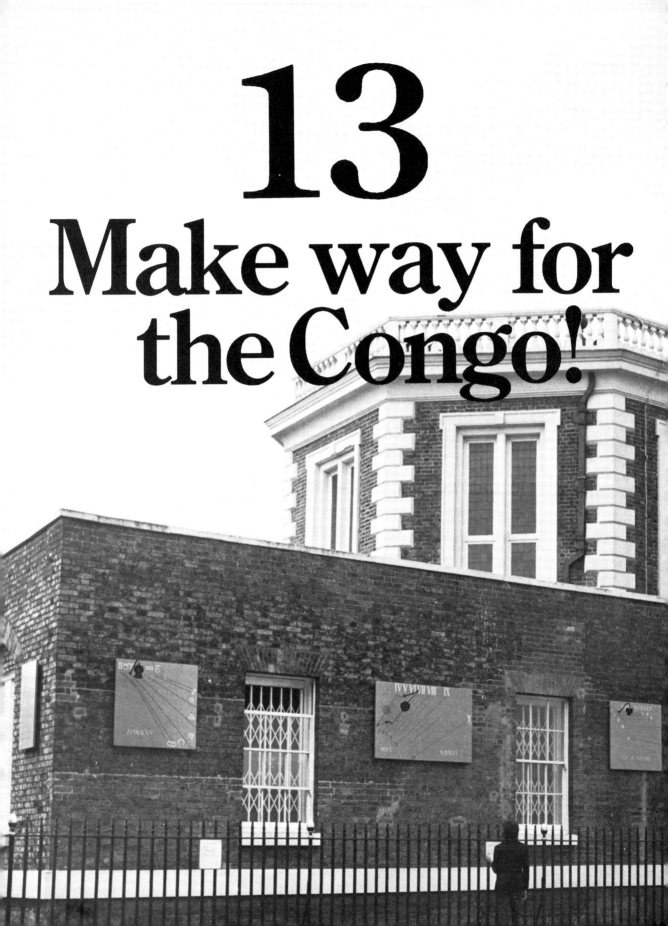

13
Make way for the Congo!

Have you ever seen one of the world's larger telescopes dangling in mid-air on the end of a chain? I have, and *The Sky at Night* was there to film it. It happened in October 1971, and was the culmination of a peculiar and in some ways slightly comic story.

The Royal Greenwich Observatory was founded in 1675, by express order of King Charles II, who may have had his little weaknesses but who was a determined and highly capable monarch with a marked sense of humour and a love of science. (Typically, he paid for the original Observatory buildings by selling old and decayed gunpowder to the French.) The chosen site was Greenwich Park, and it was here that the first Astronomer Royal, the Rev. John Flamsteed, laboured away in order to produce a new star catalogue for the use of British seamen, who at that time had an irritating knack of losing their way as soon as they were out of sight of land. Of course it is inconvenient if you set out for Morocco and end up in Iceland instead, but Flamsteed's catalogue improved the situation considerably, even though he was short-staffed and had to make do with the help of 'a silly, surly labourer' who rejoiced in the name of Cuthbert.

This is no place to tell the story of Greenwich, so let us pass straight on to the nineteenth century and the régime of a formidable Astronomer Royal named George Biddell Airy. Airy had succeeded the Rev. John Pond, who had believed firmly in doing nothing at all, and Airy had set out to re-establish the Royal Observatory as a leader in the astronomical field. He succeeded admirably, but he had his foibles. He was a stickler for Order and Discipline, and even when the nights were hopelessly cloudy he used to prowl around the telescope domes after dark, checking that the observers were at their posts, and

▶ *The Old Royal Observatory in Greenwich Park. The original was designed by Sir Christopher Wren. Note the Time-ball, dropped every day to indicate noon.*

growling, 'You are there, aren't you?' (It is said that his ghost still does the rounds, though I have never seen anything unusual myself.) On one occasion Airy apparently spent a complete afternoon in the cellars with a stack of empty boxes, painstakingly labelling each one 'Empty'.

In 1846 the hunt was on for a new planet beyond the orbit of the then farthest-known member of the Sun's family, Uranus. Mathematicians had a shrewd idea of where it might be; in France, the position of the unknown world had been worked out by Urbain Le Verrier, arguably the rudest man in the whole of Europe, while similar calculations had been undertaken in England by John Couch Adams of Cambridge. All that needed to be done was to search in the right place. There was no telescope at Greenwich capable of such a task, and after a long delay Airy delegated it to Professor James Challis at the Cambridge Observatory. Challis, frankly, made a complete hash of it, so that by the time he checked his observations the planet we now call Neptune had been identified from Berlin, on the basis of Le Verrier's work.

This almost caused an international incident, and Airy was strongly criticized. It was probably the Neptune episode which induced him to obtain a large telescope for Greenwich itself. He ordered one — a 12¾-inch refractor; that is to say, a telescope with a main lens 12¾ inches across. It was installed during the 1850s, and was set up on a massive mount consisting of two giant piers supporting the axis carrying the actual tube. The larger pier was 24 feet high, and weighed five and a half tons.

The telescope worked well, but in 1893 it was replaced by a new one placed on the same mounting. This larger instrument had a 28-inch lens, with a tube length not far short of thirty feet. It was so much bigger than its predecessor that it would not fit into the original dome, and modifications were made, so that the revised dome bulged outward so as to accommodate the telescope; the result was appropriately named the Onion Dome. It had an iron framework, and a covering of papier-mâché, which does not sound very substantial but which proved to be quite adequate.

Things went smoothly until 1939, when the war broke out and most scientific work came to an abrupt halt. The object-glass of the telescope was taken out and stored in a safe place, which was lucky because in 1944 the Germans were unfriendly enough to drop a bomb which more or less disposed of the Onion Dome. The 28-inch was not re-erected there after the end of the war, because by that time plans were well advanced for shifting all the observing equipment from Greenwich Park to a new site.

Greenwich had become unsuitable because of the spread of

▶ *The Onion Dome at Greenwich, 1984; it now contains the 28-in refractor which has come home from Herstmonceux. It is rather more substantial than the old papier-mâché dome which was so unkindly treated by the Luftaffe.*

London; the original dark skies had been replaced by glowing smog. Accordingly, the telescopes were shifted to the calm of Herstmonceux in Sussex, where the lovely old Castle was taken over as the main headquarters and domes sprouted in the grounds like mushrooms. One dome accommodated the 28-inch, and work began once more.

However, the emphasis had already been changed to large reflecting or mirror telescopes, and the 28-inch did not fit into the overall scene. The Royal Greenwich Observatory, Herstmonceux, did not really want it. On the other hand, they did want the dome which housed it, because a new reflector had been obtained. Originally this instrument had been ordered by the Congo Government; but after a series of coups and revolutions which I do not understand any better than anyone else, the Congo decided that astronomy was superfluous. More importantly, the telescope had not been paid for, so that the RGO was able to acquire it. The obvious place for it was the dome occupied by the 28-inch.

This also was in order, because the Old Royal Observatory in Greenwich Park had been turned into a museum, and had already been saying, 'Please can we have our telescope back?' Everything was arranged amicably, and all that remained to be done was to shift the telescope from Herstmonceux to Greenwich. This is where I became involved, though only as an onlooker.

The telescope could not be taken out through the door of the dome. It was much, much too large. The mounting had to be taken out too, and in view of its weight and mass this was a considerable problem. Finally it was decided that the only way to achieve success was to haul telescope and mounting out through the slit in the roof of the dome, using a powerful crane.

118

The clearance was no more than a few inches, even when the equipment had been taken apart as completely as possible, and the slightest error of judgment would have resulted in a nasty crunch.

The *Sky at Night* team arrived on 17 October, complete with cameras and recording equipment. Unfortunately, a gale blew up, as though ordered by a malevolent Nature, and this meant that the whole operation had to be postponed. The winds were still strong on the 18th, and tempers became frayed; the crane was waiting, and so were we, but conditions were quite impossible. Then, on the 19th, the wind-force dropped, and it was decided to take the risk and go ahead.

The telescope came first. It was gripped by the massive crane, and was eased slowly towards the slit. From below I could see it swinging, and I wondered whether it would pass through, but at last it was clear, and as I dashed outside I could see the vast refractor poised high in the air: I made haste to photograph it, which was lucky because the official archivist had become tired of waiting and had gone home. The telescope was lowered; then came the piers, which were even trickier to manœuvre. It was a relief when the lifting-out process was complete, and the telescope and its mounting lay safely on the grass. Loading it on to a truck was relatively easy, and a day or so later the 28-inch was back home in Greenwich Park, ready to be reinstalled in the new, more substantial version of the Onion Dome.

Certainly it was an unusual story, and it had an unusual ending, because the Congo Telescope proved to be completely useless! Nothing could be done about it, and it remains one of astronomy's most celebrated white elephants. However, the 28-inch is back in commission, and has not suffered from its travels. I know this, because in its previous site I often used it for my Moon-mapping. And I will never forget the sight of it dangling in mid-air, looking for all the world like a huge gun.

◀ *Swinging the Greenwich 28-in refractor clear of the dome at Herstmonceux.*

14
Midsummer
with the
Druids

ow and then *The Sky at Night* delves into the past — not often, because we like to be topical, but frequently enough to show that Henry Ford was wrong in claiming that history is bunk. One such occasion was in June 1972, when we set out to film sunrise over Stonehenge at the time of the summer solstice.

Stonehenge is one of the world's most famous ancient monuments, and the great stone circle is familiar to countless people. It was built long ago. I do not propose to go into details here, if only because they are too controversial, but I must stress that Stonehenge was the work of the somewhat mysterious Beaker People, and has nothing to do with the Druids. The Druid cult did not reach Britain until many centuries after the completion of the monument, and there is not the slightest evidence that they ever used it for their ceremonies; in time, they are as remote from Stonehenge as we are from King Canute. However, the modern Druids are fascinated by it, and each year, on the morning of Midsummer Day, they congregate there, suitably attired in white robes.

According to tradition, the Midsummer Sun rises directly above the Heel Stone, a huge sandstone block which lies outside the main circle and not far from the busy A303. This has been taken to indicate that Stonehenge was a primitive astronomical observatory, built as a check on the calendar. More recently it has been claimed that Stonehenge was nothing more nor less than an early form of computer, used to predict eclipses of the Sun and Moon.

To recapitulate: a solar eclipse happens when the Moon passes in front of the Sun, while a lunar eclipse is caused by the entry of the Moon into the shadow cast by the Earth. Stonehenge includes a circle of 56 holes, known as Aubrey

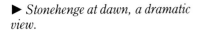
▶ *Stonehenge at dawn, a dramatic view.*

Holes after the somewhat eccentric investigator who first drew attention to them, and Professor Gerald Hawkins, who has written exhaustively on the subject, proposed the theory that the Aubrey Holes were markers, so that a movable stone could be shifted round them from one year to another. When the midwinter full moon rose over the Heel Stone a lunar eclipse was quite likely, and the movable stone would by then have been placed in the appropriate Aubrey Hole.

My objection to this was that if the builders of Stonehenge knew enough to build a relatively elaborate computer of this type they would have had no need to construct it at all; they would simply have worked it out. However, Gerald was not alone in his views. He was supported by Sir Fred Hoyle, among others, and we felt that the whole subject merited a programme, particularly as Gerald happened to be in England and was quite willing to join in.

Naturally, we wanted to film the midsummer sunrise. This fell on 21 June, but we had learned enough to keep our options open, and we arrived at the site on the 20th, ready to go. However, there were bureaucratic problems to be overcome first. Even at that period, before the unwelcome emergence of hippy convoys, Stonehenge needed protection, and around midsummer entry to the monument itself was restricted — a wise precaution, because in the past the stones have been damaged by vandals. Of course, the members of the BBC team had special passes, but most other people were banned from the immediate neighbourhood, and barbed-wire fences had been set up on the orders of the Ministry of Defence.

Our team included perhaps a dozen persons as well as Gerald Hawkins and myself, but we had been staying at a local hotel, and there were others who were anxious to join us: the hotel manager, the manager's daughter, the manager's daughter's boy-friend and so on. They had no passes, and had to slip by the Guardian of the Monument, a fearsome and very large lady from the Ministry who sat in the only entrance like Horatio defending the bridge. Her attention had to be diverted while the extra onlookers slid through; after all, they were doing no harm, and we could vouch for them.

On the morning of the 20th we were all ready for the Sun to appear. The forecast for Midsummer itself was not good, and so far as we were concerned this did not matter much, because the position of sunrise shows little change for several consecutive days. The sky was clear, and we were able to get good shots of the Sun as it rose majestically above the Heel Stone, after which we filmed the rest of the Stonehenge part of the programme and returned to our hotel for breakfast with the intention of reshooting on the following day.

This time we were not alone. I have already mentioned the modern Druids, who are blissfully oblivious of the fact that their alleged predecessors were not Stonehenge-minded. They turned up in their dozens, looking like white spectres, and I could not help being reminded of the Chorus of Ancestors in Ruddigore Castle; I half expected to see Sir Despard Murgatroyd at any moment. Predictably, it rained — and rained — and rained. The Druids chanted and waved their arms, dripping mournfully as the water poured down. I have never seen such a sodden collection of people, and even their spirits were dampened in the end, so that the mystic ceremony simply petered out. We filmed what we could, but when we saw the results we realized that we would have to make do with what we had obtained twenty-four hours earlier.

The rest of the programme dealt not with Stonehenge but with a neighbouring monument, Woodhenge. This is much less well known, because no ancient stones remain, and at first sight Woodhenge looks like a small forest of concrete blocks which, needless to say, are modern and have been erected in the old post-holes. Unlike Stonehenge, Woodhenge is not circular, and the posts are arranged in complicated egg-shaped patterns, each of which bears a mathematical relationship to the others. Gerald Hawkins maintained that the unit of length used by the old builders was regulated by the length of the human arm, and he pointed out that the inner ring can just be spanned by twenty

▼ *The Druids, just before the rains came. They looked most impressive, even if they have as much to do with Stonehenge as I have with Mesopotamian economics.*

◄ With Dr Gerald Hawkins at Stonehenge, when we proved some intriguing scientific facts even though I am not now sure quite what they were.

people standing along the blocks with their arms outstretched; the second can just be spanned by thirty people, and so on out to the final ring (eighty people). To test this out, we called in a school party visiting the site while we were there. The boys entered willingly into the spirit of it all, and we had a great deal of fun, though exactly what we managed to prove I do not pretend to know.

As a final comment, I must record a remark made by one American tourist to his wife just after the Druids had departed on midsummer morning. They were looking at Stonehenge, and I overheard the following classic criticism: 'Yes, it's a great monument, but what a pity they put it so near the road!' You probably won't believe that, but I can assure you that it is true.

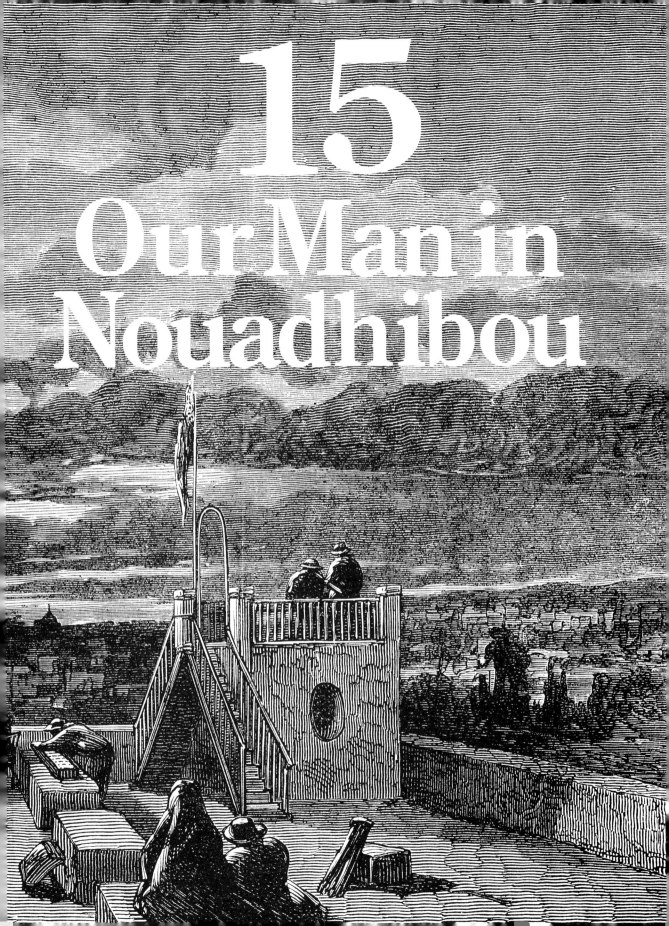

15
Our Man in
Nouadhibou

I don't want to give the impression that *The Sky at Night* has been obsessed with eclipse expeditions. Far from it; we have mounted only two full-scale efforts, not counting my solo journey to Siberia. But I really cannot omit the 1973 'eclipse of the century', because some episodes during it were frankly hilarious.

I call it 'the eclipse of the century', as everyone else did at the time, because the length of totality was over seven minutes, which is practically the maximum possible. We did not want to miss the opportunity, but it meant going abroad, because from England only a tiny segment of the Sun was due to be obscured, and casual observers could not be expected to notice it at all. The track of totality began off the African coast and then crossed the Dark Continent, passing through the states of Mauritania, Mali, Niger, Chad, Sudan and Kenya before tapering off in the Indian Ocean. At that stage I knew very little about any of these countries, but we had to make a decision, and we investigated as carefully as we could.

From the point of view of climate and length of totality, Mali seemed to be ideal. (Do you know just where Mali is? I didn't, until I looked it up.) Unfortunately, there were some drawbacks. Roads and communications in general were said to be conspicuous only by their absence, but there was also a violently left-wing Government to be considered. We were warned that although we might be able to get into the country, it would be much more difficult to get out, and there was a danger of our being impounded as dangerous capitalist agents. Prudently, we crossed Mali off our list.

The Cape Verde Islands, off the African mainland, were much more inviting, but after consulting the weather-men we established that complete cloud-cover at that time of the year (June) was practically certain, and, reluctantly, we abandoned Cape Verde. We next looked at Kenya, but the length of totality was less, and the meteorological outlook was rather uncertain. (In the event, a major expedition did go there, only to be met with a hostile reception from the local inhabitants, who were convinced that the white men had arrived in order to put out the Sun!) Next on our list was Mauritania, but again facilities were poor, and the prospects were not encouraging. Finally, Pat Owtram came up with the bright idea of transmitting direct from the deck of a ship.

Here too there were obvious drawbacks, but there was a good deal to be said on the plus side, particularly as the good ship *Monte Umbe* was going to the centre of the track in any case, carrying a couple of hundred mad astronomers; the expedition had been organized by the Explorers Travel Club, and I had already been invited to join it. So we settled for the

◀ (previous page) *An engraving of an American expedition to view the solar eclipse of 1871 from Xeres, now Jerez, in Spain.*

128

Monte Umbe, knowing full well that rough seas at the vital moment would prove a major hazard.

But how could we get our films back to the studio in time for transmission the same evening? We could arrange for a link-man in the Television Centre studio, but our films and my on-the-spot commentary were essential. The answer seemed to be to get the material flown back direct from the nearest port, which was, of course, in Mauritania.

Mauritania itself is almost entirely Sahara Desert, and has only two towns of any size. One is the capital, Nouakchott, which then consisted mainly of tents (I gather that the Prime Minister had a bigger tent than anyone else). The other is Nouadhibou, at the very edge of the coastal desert, and I asked whether the BBC had any representative there. The date, please remember, was 1973.

'Yes,' was the reply. 'We do have our man in Nouadhibou, and no doubt he'll be able to help.'

'Can we telephone him?' I asked.

This seemed reasonable enough, so we tried; in fact we tried for a complete morning, with a complete lack of success. All we could get down the line was a series of depressing squeaks. Finally I became somewhat suspicious. 'When did the BBC last contact our man in Nouadhibou?'

The answer was . . . 1948!

Presumably he had been on the payroll ever since, but we consigned him to outer darkness and managed to get in touch with the local officials, who did their best. We also called in a local pilot, and in the end it all worked out well.

A week before the date of the eclipse we trooped on board the *Monte Umbe*, joining many old friends — mainly amateur astronomers, but some professionals as well. It was a delightful ship in every way, and I am very sorry that it has been scrapped now.

We were introduced to the captain, who was Spanish and who was unfailingly helpful and courteous. His name was Captain Mirallave, though I am quite sure that he was really the Duke of Plaza-Toro in disguise. When we asked how close he hoped to get to the centre of the eclipse track, he gave a knowing smile. 'The waters in that part of the ocean have not been well charted,' he said. 'There are two maps, one French and one Spanish. The French map shows many dangerous rocks. The Spanish map shows no rocks at all. I will be using the Spanish map.'

Well — how could I, as a mere airman, make any comment? It was, however, reassuring to know that one of our amateur astronomers on board was Commander Henry Hatfield, RN, who had been the Navy's leading hydrographer. And let me add that the *Monte Umbe* did get to exactly the right place at exactly the right time, avoiding all contact with French rocks; full marks to the Duke of Plaza-Toro.

We worked out our programme, in which we featured the other eclipse parties. One expedition, of special interest, involved a Concorde aircraft. The Moon's shadow flashes along at a tremendous rate, which is why the length of totality as seen from any point on earth is so brief, but Concorde has enough speed to fly beneath the shadow, keeping pace with it. The plan was to take off from the airfield at Las Palmas, in the Canary Islands, and fly along at a height of 55,000 feet. This meant that most of the dense layers of atmosphere would lie below, and the Concorde observers could expect to have a 'totality' lasting for over half an hour, enabling them to make continuous records and note any short-term changes in the corona and other features — something which had never been done before. Dr John Beckman, one of our regular *Sky at Night* guests, was on the Concorde, and promised to let us have his results as soon as he knew them himself.

The Concorde had to be modified to some extent, and three holes were bored in the roof to accommodate the astronomical equipment. One thought occurred to me. I knew that such a team based inland from Nouadhibou was planning to launch an upper-atmosphere rocket during totality, and I had the fleeting fear that if they dispatched it at the wrong moment there might be four holes in the Concorde. Luckily, these misgivings turned out to be groundless.

The journey to the site was most enjoyable, though I did have one personal crisis. We stopped off for a few hours at Las Palmas, and were able to look inside the waiting Concorde and take some film of it; then I went into the town (which qualifies as a concrete jungle these days) with the intention of telephoning my mother on her eighty-seventh birthday. I hired a local taxi, and set off. In Las Palmas I made my call — by some miracle I got straight through; it was much easier than ringing up Surrey from Sussex — and then re-entered the taxi to go back to the dock. The driver accelerated out into the main road — and crashed headlong into another taxi. Disaster! Police swarmed round, pointing their fingers at me. 'Witness, witness,' they seemed to be saying, and I had to do some swift thinking. If I were held up in Las Palmas I would miss the eclipse, because I could hardly expect either it or the *Monte Umbe* to wait for me.

I cannot speak Spanish, so I broke into my decidedly unorthodox French. While the police were arguing with the taxi-drivers and with each other I dashed round the corner of the street, hailed another cab, and demanded to be taken to the dock. Fortunately, the driver obeyed; I lost no time in getting back on board, and hid prudently in my cabin until we sailed a couple of hours later. Fond as I am of the Canaries, I was glad on this occasion to see them receding in the distance.

By 30 June we had reached a point some 24 miles from the Mauritanian coast, right in the central track. The main problem, of course, was stability. A swaying deck is not the ideal place to set up a telescope or a camera, and the various participants had made all kinds of devices to counteract ship movement. Some of the instruments were mounted on gimbals; one telescope was fixed to a piece of mechanism which looked like a demented windmill; weights, pendulums (?pendula?) and other ingenious dodges were much in evidence. I had considerable respect for Horace Dall, the famous optical expert, who scornfully rejected all such things and merely planned to lie flat on his back, balancing his camera on his nose. I had no telescope myself, because I knew from the outset that I would be fully occupied with my television commentary.

Elaborate rehearsals were held, to the bewilderment of the ship's crew. I well remember the efforts of the hostesses and ship's organizers to marshal us. 'There will be deck games at 11.30 this morning . . . ' And shortly afterwards, plaintively: 'There will be no deck games this morning.' Bingo and other attractions fared no better. I was particularly sorry for the ship's photographer, who found, to his despair, that he was unwanted because everyone on board had at least three cameras. Even on the morning of the eclipse, deck games were still announced, but it would have been rather difficult to hold them, because every square inch of deck-space was occupied.

I also remember the Case of the Orbiting Professor. We had set up a rehearsal sequence, and were about to talk to Commander Hatfield when we saw a large figure zooming in towards us — that of an American professor who believed in taking regular exercise, and made a habit of achieving twenty orbits round the main deck before breakfast (you could even set your watch by him). He was just about to blunder into our line of sight when Patricia Wood, our director, spotted him and made a wild wave. One of the sound assistants reached out to grab him, but too late; he continued on his way and then, realizing the enormity of his crime, stood right in front of the camera and took ten minutes to apologize. As our rehearsal time was strictly limited, we all felt an almost uncontrollable desire to tip him overboard.

On eclipse day itself the weather was clear, and mercifully, the sea was so calm that the various stablizing devices were not needed. There was an air of tremendous tension as the light faded; then came the onrush of the Moon's shadow, and the sky turned a curious mauve colour. Two planets could be seen,

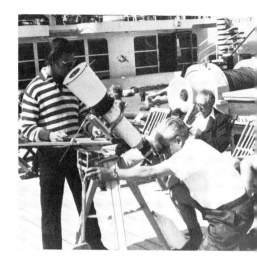

▲ *Preparations on the Monte Umbe, for the 1973 eclipse; Commander Hatfield adjusts his 'stabilizer', which in the event he didn't have to use. Every square inch of deck was occupied!*

▲ *One of the many 'dodges' to stabilize a telescope on deck during the eclipse of 1973. This one took the form of a large weight to which the telescope was attached.*

Venus below the Sun and Saturn above, though I could not make out any of the stars.

With over seven minutes' totality, we had a real chance to draw breath, and it was all very different from our fleeting 37 seconds at Yurgamysh. I concentrated upon the commentary; beside me the camera team, led by Philip Bonham-Carter, was hard at work getting the best possible shots. Then, suddenly, the diamond-ring effect shone out, and the sunlight came back as the shadow of the Moon sped away across the ocean.

It was then that I realized that I had dropped my small hand-camera. I stooped down to pick it up — and my trousers split across the back. It was my bad luck that one of our photographic experts happened to be ideally placed to 'shoot' me. He later showed me the picture. I never managed to obtain a copy of it, but at least I am one of a very few people on record as having split his trousers during totality.

There were a few disasters. Someone had a faulty film; another enthusiast took forty pictures of the corona under ideal conditions, only to find that his lens-hood had been in position the whole time, and so on, but in general the results were good. Not so with the Nouadhibou rocket, which had been sent up to take pictures of the corona in ultra-violet light; the de-spinning mechanism of the rocket refused to work, and all the film was blank. A team in inland Mauritania had mixed fortunes, partly because of a sandstorm and partly because the nice, friendly inhabitants surrounded the members of the expedition just before totality and proceeded to hurl rocks at them. In Niger a violent dust-storm blacked out the eclipse completely. On the credit side, the Concorde flight was faultless, and John Beckman and his colleagues achieved everything that they had set out to do.

With totality over, our first need was to get our films back to London. We went into Nouadhibou, contacted the pilot, and waved him off. Then we had a few hours to look round the town itself, which I can honestly say is the most ghastly place I have ever seen. The only industry takes the form of an evil-smelling fertilizer factory, there are flies everywhere, and the sand gets into your mouth and up your nose. Add the scorching heat, the glare and the universal dirt, and you will appreciate what I mean.

I recalled all this during the ship's concert, given on the last evening of our voyage home and just before we bade a regretful good-bye to the *Monte Umbe*. Normally, the final concert is presented by the ship's entertainment staff, but this time we took it over. My own contribution, right at the end, consisted of a music-hall turn ending with a song about Nouadhibou, which I wrote and composed specially for the occasion and which was given its one and only public performance. I reproduce it here just in case anyone wants to try it out at a concert in the Royal Festival Hall:

BOO, BOO, NOUADHIBOU¹

We walked into the desert sun,
The day had only just begun,
We'd heard such glowing rumours of the place.
We looked for sheikhs on Arab steeds,
And women dressed in gorgeous beads,
But when we saw what we had got to face —

(*Chorus*)   Boo, boo, Nouadhibou,
       We're glad you're far away.
       True, true, Nouadhibou.
       You told us we could stay.
       But pooh, pooh, Nouadhibou.
       It's time to say 'Good-day';
       So toodle-oo, Nouadhibou.
       Shall we come back? Nay, nay!

We watched with glazed and goggling eyes
As multitudes of desert flies
Surrounded us and nibbled at our coats.
We dodged the crowd of market boys
Who tried to sell us junk and toys,
And cursed us as we ran back to our boats:

(*Chorus*)

And as we leave this sandy land
It isn't hard to understand
That we will come here never, never more.
One visit here was quite enough,
And Mauritania now can stuff
Its sand back whence it came in days of yore:

(*Chorus*)

    I am hardly a great lyricist, and I am certainly not a virtuoso pianist, but we were all in a good mood, and I can remember every detail of that concert.
    So farewell, *Monte Umbe*; farewell, the Duke of Plaza-Toro. It all seems aeons ago, but it was certainly one of my very happiest moments in *The Sky at Night*.

16
Low Moon, High Moon

▲ *With Sir Alan Herbert, as we prepared a programme about Sundials, with the Thames in the background — and were plagued by a wretched model aircraft which persistently buzzed us.*

As I've said, there are occasions when everything seems to go wrong. This is particularly so in my case, because I am an absolute Jonah when it comes to mechanical equipment. I have absolutely no practical skill myself, and machines seem to know it, so that even television recorders break down the instant I set foot in the studio. I remember one episode when two mobile cameras actually met head-on during live transmission. I could see them moving purposefully on collision course, but there was little that I could do about it, and they duly crunched against each other, sending out little sparks in all directions. On the monitor before me I saw myself sliding out of view through the bottom of the screen, still talking hard.

More infuriating still was a hazard which we encountered when presenting a programme about sundials. With me was Sir Alan Herbert, who knew a great deal about sundials and had even written a book about them. For reasons which I cannot recall, we had set out our equipment on the banks of the Thames near Alan's home, and this is where we proposed to do the interview. Just as we were ready to go, a radio-controlled model aeroplane zoomed over us, going 'Bzzzzzz! Bzzzzzz!' in a manner which made our sound recordist call an abrupt halt. Waiting until the intruder had withdrawn, we set up again . . . 'Bzzzzzz!' No less than eight times we called for 'Action', and each time we were thwarted by that wretched model. We seriously thought about shooting it down, and after an hour's delay we had reached the limit of our patience. When the Sun disappeared behind a bank of cloud we had to admit defeat, and that was the end of our filming for the day.

Another programme which seemed at first to be dogged by all manner of unexpected problems proved in the end to be one of our greatest successes, because it provided information which is still quoted in scientific journals. It had to do with the celebrated Moon Illusion, which had been known for at least two thousand years but which has not been fully explained yet.

Watch the Moon rising, and you may think that it looks huge, at least the size of a dinner-plate. When it climbs above the horizon it appears to shrink, until when high in the sky it is no more than a tiny disc. Actually, the low moon is no bigger than the high moon, but the illusion is very marked, and was described by Ptolemy of Alexandria around the year 150. Ptolemy had an explanation. When the Moon is low, he said, we observe it across 'filled space', and can compare it with any trees or houses which happen to lie in the same direction. By the time the Moon has risen high there is nothing with which to compare it, and it is seen across 'empty' space, so that it looks small.

This sounds reasonable enough, but it is not the complete

◀ (previous page) *The Moon appears to be remarkably large as it first clears the horizon. This is an illusion which we don't fully understand.*

answer, so we decided to take another gamble with the weather and try out a really original demonstration. I can claim no credit for working it out. That was the brainwave of another friend of long standing, Professor Richard Gregory, who knows more about optical illusions than anyone else.

We chose 18 September 1973 because this was the date of Harvest Moon, a term which I must explain because so many people do not understand what it means. The Moon, of course, takes part in the daily east-to-west rotation of the sky which is due to the real rotation of the Earth from west to east. In addition, the Moon has its own movement against the starry background, as you can easily check next time the Moon is on view and you take the trouble to watch it for an hour or so. Obviously, then, the Moon will rise later each night. The interval between the rising-time on successive nights is know as the 'retardation', and may amount to the best part of an hour.

As an approximation, it is good enough to say that the Moon moves against the stars by the same distance every night. The retardation depends, then, on the angle which the apparent path of the Moon makes with the horizon, and in August, September and October this angle is at its shallowest, so the retardation may be no more than fifteen minutes. I hope this is clear. In the programme, I gave a demonstration coming to the same thing.

September is harvest time, and farmers used to find the continued presence of the full moon helpful, because it meant that they could work late (this, of course, was before the advent of trade unionism). The full moon of late September came to be called Harvest Moon, while that of the following month was Hunter's Moon. It was (and is) often believed that the Harvest Moon is particularly large when rising, which is why we chose it. However, I took pains to point out that Harvest Moon is in no way exceptional, and if it happens to fall at a moment when the Moon is at its greatest distance from the Earth it may even be smaller than average.

At the start of the programme I outlined the various theories proposed to account for the illusion, starting with Ptolemy's. I disposed of the idea that dustiness in the lower atmosphere may blur the Moon's edge and enlarge the disc, and also a less convincing idea that the Moon looks large when low down because more of its light is absorbed by the atmosphere and it seems fainter. I then explained that we were setting out to compare not the *real* relative sizes of the low and high moons, but their *apparent* relative sizes, which was not the same thing at all.

We waited until dark, and then went down to Selsey beach, which is a mere five hundred yards down the country lane off which my house stands. I am not going to claim that it is a beautiful beach; it isn't, and the shore is as flat as several hats, but it is a pleasant place, and normally the water is clean and free from pollution. I might have known that things would be different that night . . .

Richard Gregory's apparatus consisted mainly of a rotatable mirror in which the moonlight could be reflected. We also had an artificial moon, a few feet away. Using an iris, we could alter the size of the artificial moon, and by rotating the mirror we could alter the apparent altitude of the real Moon. Richard operated the equipment, and I did the observing. First, the real Moon was 'brought down' until it was side by side with the artificial one, and the iris was adjusted until I judged that the two discs were equal in size. Then the real Moon was raised. As I half expected, it seemed to shrink, and the artificial image had to be reduced by at least 10 per cent until the two appeared equal again. Note that there was no real change in size; as I have said, we were measuring how large the two discs looked, not how large they really were.

Quite obviously the experiment confirmed the reality of the illusion, but we could not leave it at that. There had been suggestions that people with the sight of only one eye were not subject to the illusion at all; one of our sound recordists nobly volunteered to cover up his left eye for a couple of hours before the programme, but the illusion was still there. Another idea was that the low Moon looked large because it was observed 'straight on', so to speak. I was persuaded to stand on my head, which I managed to do with considerable difficulty and some assistance from the television crew. By this time we had quite an audience, and the sight of my glaring at the Moon from an upside-down position created the general impression that I was as nutty as the proverbial fruit-cake.

We had other problems, too. One of the generators in our power supply was dying, and periodically it petered out, plunging much of the scene into relative darkness. Moths were a constant hazard; they were attracted by the glare, and committed hara-kiri in the lamps, choking them so completely that they had to be shovelled out every few minutes. The tide was coming in quickly, bringing with it a quantity of evil-smelling seaweed which I have never seen at Selsey before or since. Mercifully, a kindly friend from a nearby hotel brought down plentiful supplies of sandwiches and drink. We needed them, particularly the drink.

By two o'clock in the morning we were fairly happy with the results of our experiment, and the Moon was shining down from on high, looking much smaller than it had done a few hours earlier. Then I had another idea. Most people always visualize the Moon as looking much bigger than it really does, as you can appreciate from almost any picture of a landscape illuminated by moonlight. Everything seemed to call for more audience participation.

Without claiming that Selsey Beach is a romantic setting, or that it can be compared with (say) Hawaii or the South Seas, it has its points, particularly during a warm and balmy September night. Not far away I could see figures lying on the shingle, oblivious of the odour of the weed or, indeed, anything except each other. With some trepidation I approached the nearest couple, and asked whether they would mind taking part in a scientific experiment. Would they, please, choose a stone which they thought would be just big enough to cover the Moon when the stone was held at arm's-length?

Had they taken umbrage I wouldn't have been particularly surprised; in similar circumstances I believe I might have done. Luckily, they entered into the spirit of the thing, and, predictably, selected a stone which was too large by a factor of about fifty. Other couples clustered round, attracted by the buzz of conversation, and before long there were groups of people all holding up stones and squinting in the direction of the Moon. It must have been a curious spectacle, and I am only sorry that we could not film it; by that time the generator had packed up completely, and in any case all the lamps were choked by dead moths.

We finally called a halt at about 3 a.m., and bade goodnight to our willing helpers, who were probably glad to be left in peace. Next day we sat down to analyse all the results.

First, and most telling of all, Richard's apparatus had confirmed the status of the illusion. There was no question of any actual alteration in size, so that everything depended upon how large the two discs looked. Secondly, we had eliminated all the classic explanations of the illusion, apart possibly from Ptolemy's, and even there we had misgivings. All in all, we concluded that in all probability the human brain was playing tricks. When the Moon is seen across filled space we unconsciously assume that it is relatively close, whereas when it is high in the sky it deceives us into thinking that it is farther away — and so must seem smaller.

Whether this is the full answer I don't know, but at least our experiment was worth trying, despite the seaweed and the moths. Next time the sky is clear and the Moon is full, check for yourself, perhaps by choosing a stone and seeing whether you fall into the same trap as our beach friends did. You can even try standing on your head, though if you do so in public I recommend that you station someone on guard to prevent your being summarily arrested and carted off to the nearest psychiatric ward.

17
Near-misses

I have often been asked how I have managed to keep up an unbroken record of *Sky at Night* appearances over the past thirty years. 'What about holidays? And what happens if you're ill?' are two of the most usual questions. Also, 'Why don't you pre-record a couple of programmes to hold in reserve in case anything goes wrong?'

So far as holidays are concerned, I simply don't need them. My 'work' and my hobby are the same thing, and I can safely say that since I emerged from the RAF in 1945 I haven't done a day's work in my life; neither do I ever intend to do so. However, in the *Sky at Night* timings we have had several narrow escapes, the first of which dates back to our old live-programme, black-and-white days of 1960.

The topic was meteorites, which are chunks of solid material coming from space and ending their careers on the surface of the Earth. Note, please, that a meteorite is not simply a large meteor, but is entirely different in origin. Shooting-star meteors are cometary débris, and are of dust-grain size, so that they burn out well above ground-level. A meteorite is much bigger and more massive, and may be made of iron, stone or a combination of both. There is no known connection with comets; meteorites seem to come from the asteroid zone, and there is probably no distinction between a large meteorite and a small asteroid. For example, the object which hit the Arizonan desert over 20,000 years ago and left a gaping crater there might be put into either category.

My guest on this programme was Dr G.J.H. ('Jo') McCall, one of our foremost experts on the subject of meteorites. Both of us lived well out of London, Jo in the Midlands and I in East Grinstead, on the borders of Sussex and Surrey. We were due to meet at Lime Grove at the usual time of three o'clock. According to schedule, we would sort out all the visual material, have a prolonged rehearsal, go and eat in the BBC Club, and then do the programme live at around 9.30 (we had earlier viewing slots in those dim and distant days). Unfortunately, the whole of England was enwrapped in dense fog. When I woke up in the morning I couldn't even see the tree a few yards from my front door. I rang Jo, and found the situation there just as bad.

Needless to say, the train service had come to a total stop. British Rail services in 1960 were not so awful as they are today, and the main lines still used steam trains instead of the modern Diesels which stop working at the slightest hint of bad weather, but the East Grinstead line was poor at the best of times, and I knew at once that I would have to make my own way.

I had an ancient motor-cycle, a 1929 Triumph, which was known to all and sundry as 'Vesuvius' for obvious reasons. I had bought it shortly after the war for the princely sum of £9, and it had served me well; in fact it continued to do so until, to my deep and genuine distress, it was stolen in the early 1970s. Vesuvius was the only solution to my problem. I put on my gear, and set out to crawl the thirty miles to Shepherd's Bush.

The fog was of the pea-soup variety all the way, and it was not a journey I enjoyed; I think I must have been the only moving object on the road. Eventually I reached the studio, and then, at half-past three, Jo McCall arrived. Paul Johnstone was already there, with his secretary and his assistant Stephanie Johnston (the similarity of the two names often caused confusion, made worse when they were joined by another assistant producer, Micheál Johnson). We also had one cameraman and one sound-recordist, together with a vision mixer. It was very much of a skeleton staff, but as the evening wore on the fog became thicker, and we realized that we would have to make do.

I am proud to say that we snatched victory out of impending defeat. Everyone played their part. I remember doing a piece direct to camera and then leaping across the studio floor to hold up captions while Jo took over; one of the sound-recordists doubled by operating the second camera, and so on. The entire programme went through without a hitch, and we all felt smugly satisfied. It couldn't happen today, of course, because equipment has become so complicated that no novice could handle it, but in 1960 we could cope.

There was a curious aftermath! Meteorites can be found sometimes,[1] and may be large; the holder of the heavyweight record is still lying where it fell in prehistoric times near Grootfontein in southern Africa, and nobody is likely to run away with it, because it weighs well over 60 tons. A missile of that size would cause tremendous devastation upon landing, but major impacts are very rare, and there is no reliable record of anyone having been killed by a piece of tumbling space débris. Smaller meteorites are common enough, and most museums have collections of them. During my talk with Jo McCall I happened to mention that the non-scientist would be hard pressed to tell the difference between a meteorite and an ordinary lump of mineral, so that no doubt many meteorites had been thrown away and lost to posterity.

That was an error of judgment, because everyone started to

[1] *I once went meteorite-hunting myself, in quest of a piece of the Barwell Meteorite, which flashed over England on Christmas Eve 1965 and broke up, showering fragments over areas in Leicestershire. I found a piece the size of a teapot. Of course I handed it over to a museum, but they passed it back, telling me to keep it for display and make sure that I left it to them in my will — which I have done.*

send me meteorites! They arrived in parcels, packets and by special delivery. I accumulated vast numbers of chunks of concrete, stones of all shapes and sizes, and even an iron cannon-ball which must have been left over from the Wars of the Roses. There was not one genuine meteorite among them, but I examined them carefully to make sure that I had not missed anything. One 'meteorite' baffled me for some time, because it didn't seem to fit into any general classification. It finally turned out to be a semi-fossilized Bath bun.

The fact that I have avoided missing any programmes through illness must be put down to sheer luck, but again there have been crises now and then. Once, in 1973, we were transmitting from a Manchester studio because there was no room for us in either Lime Grove or Television Centre, and I did not enjoy it, because I was down with some sort of 'flu and had a temperature of well over 103. Then, just after our twentieth anniversary programme in 1977, I had one of those wretched accidents which can happen to everybody except oneself. I slipped in the bathroom, knocked my head on the bath and jerked my spine sideways. A fraction of an inch more, and someone else would now be presenting *The Sky at Night*. I remember very little of the next fortnight, and even by the time that the next programme was due I could neither walk nor use my hands. Two good friends, Ron Maddison from Keele and Gordon Taylor from Herstmonceux, rallied round; they came to Selsey and joined me in my study, where I was planted in an armchair to make sure that my sorry state was not evident. It took me many months to recover from that incident.

There are dangers in recording *Sky at Night* programmes much ahead of transmission, because there may be urgent late news at any moment. Also, we can be unlucky with timing. This happened in 1975. Our August programme was broadcast on the 28th, and dealt with the Moon. Next night, I went out to my observatory soon after sunset, opened the dome, and looked casually around the sky to decide what to do first. There, in the constellation of Cygnus, the Swan, was a bright star which was certainly a newcomer. . . .

I watched it for long enough to ensure that I was not being tricked by a slowly moving artificial satellite, and then went indoors to ring the Royal Greenwich Observatory at Herstmonceux. 'You do know, don't you?' I said rather wearily. 'Yes,' was the reply. 'The nova was discovered by a Japanese amateur at three o'clock this afternoon.'

The nova, or new star, had been so faint on the previous night that it had passed unnoticed, and had flared up to prominence in only a few hours. Inevitably the eagle-eyed Japanese discovered it, because sunset there occurred before darkness fell over Europe. I suppose I can claim to have been an independent discoverer, but so far as I can make out I was about eighty-third on the list. A day earlier, and we could have featured it in our programme. As it was, we had to wait for a month, by which time Nova Cygni had dropped well below naked-eye visibility.

▼ *Nova Cygni, photographed in 1975.*

Strictly speaking, a nova is not a new star at all. What happens is that a formerly very faint star suffers a violent outburst, which makes it flare up by a factor of many thousands, but it does not remain bright for long. By now Nova Cygni has become so dim that even my powerful 15-inch reflector at Selsey will no longer show it.

Nowadays we prerecord our programmes either a day or so or else a few hours before transmission. But Spode's Law is always with us — so if you would like to see a brilliant comet or a flashing supernova, let me know, and I will do my best to fix a *Sky at Night* recording at least three weeks before we are due on the air.

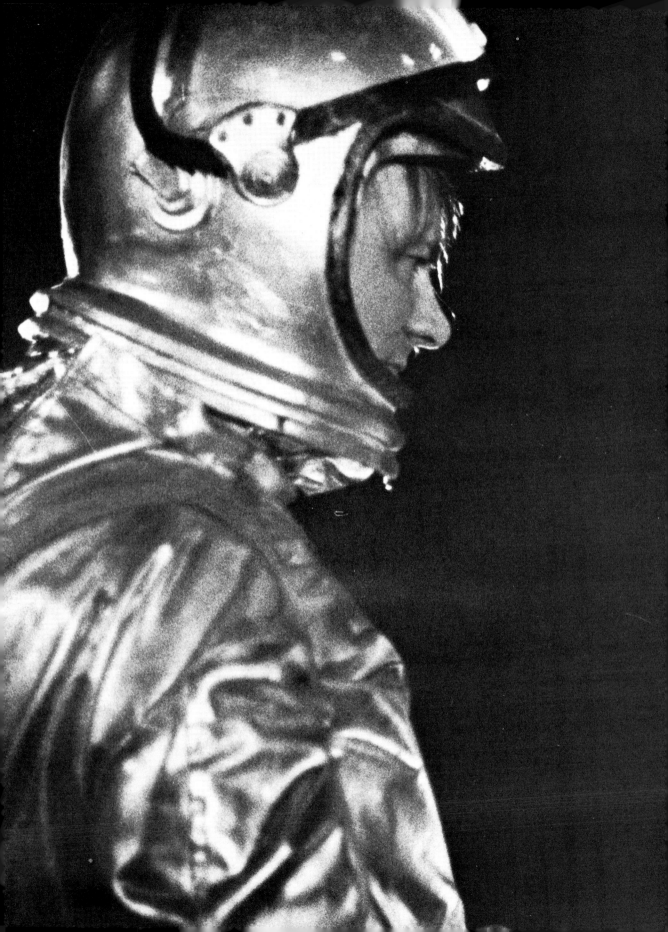

18
Unearthly
Life?

▲ *Carl Sagan, one of the world's leading thinkers on astronomy and astrophysics. I took this photo at the Jet Propulsion Laboratory in California.*

O f all the questions to be asked, perhaps the most intriguing is: 'Are we alone in the universe?' Inevitably we have devoted a good many programmes to the possibility of life on other worlds, the first occasion being as long ago as 1958, with Harlow Shapley.

Of course there have been many theories, some more convincing than others. (There have also been some remarkable claims; many years ago a reputable journal published a letter from a man who stated that with his telescope he could see large creatures walking about on the surface of the Moon. They turned out to be ants in his eyepiece.) One of the founders of the infant science of 'exobiology' is Carl Sagan, and in 1974 he joined me in the studio.

As he pointed out, our search for life must logically be confined to life of the sort we can understand. As soon as you start to talk about entirely alien forms, such as beings made of pure gold and capable of breathing pure carbon monoxide, you enter the realm of science fiction, making speculation pointless as well as endless. In our Solar System, only the Earth is suited to the development of intelligent life. (Whether intelligent life has actually appeared here is not for me to say.) Therefore we must look farther afield, and since even the nearest star beyond the Sun is well over twenty million million miles away there is no chance of dispatching a rocket there. As Carl said, the only present hope of establishing communication with an alien race is by means of radio, since radio waves move at 186,000 miles per second — the same velocity as light.

The closest stars which are at all like the Sun, and might well be expected to have planetary systems of their own, are around 11 light-years away (one light-year, the distance travelled by a ray of light in a year, is rather less than 6,000,000,000,000 miles). Send out a message, and it will reach its destination 11 years later. If some obliging radio astronomer picks it up and sends an immediate reply, it will take another 11 years to get back to us. The total interval between transmission and answer is thus 22 years, which, as I commented, is even slower than the Post Office. It means that quick-fire repartee is bound to be somewhat difficult.

When we presented that programme plans were already being made to send soft-landing vehicles to the planet Mars, in an effort to find out whether there might be any trace of life there. The discovery of living material would prove one vital point: if conditions are such that life *can* evolve it *will*. The two Vikings were launched just over a year later, in the summer of 1975, and naturally we covered them in full.

Mariner 9 of 1971 had already shown the Martian surface to be cratered and volcanic, and the attractive idea that the dark

▲ *Viking 1 on its way to Mars; a successful launch from Cape Canaveral. Though no Martians were found, the Viking project was a great success.*

areas might be old seas filled with vegetation had been abandoned. (The most prominent dark feature on Mars, the V-shaped area known as the Syrtis Major, is actually a lofty plateau.) However, there was thought to be plenty of ice, not only in the polar caps but also below ground in other areas, and the outlook did not seem to be too pessimistic. I think that most of the NASA team sincerely believed that if the Vikings worked well, they would give us our first real proof of extraterrestrial life, albeit of very lowly type.

A Viking was made up of two parts, an orbiter and a lander. The two sections crossed space together, and were still joined when their on-board rockets were fired to put them into a closed path around Mars. Then, at a command from Earth, the lander was broken free to come down on to the planet's surface, slowed partly by parachute and partly by rocket braking. Luck was needed as well as skill, because it was impossible to allow for all the rocks strewn around, and the landing speed had to be effectively zero. In a programme broadcast on 14 July 1976, a week before the touch-down of Viking 1, I was joined by Dr Garry Hunt and Dr Geoffrey Eglinton. We had some models of the Viking lander, and tested them by dropping them on to a mock-up of a red Martian plain. As Garry said, we established one important fact: 'If you drop them too hard, they break!'

Luckily, both the Vikings came down safely, avoiding all the dangerous rocks. Scoops were sent out from the grounded spacecraft, so that material could be drawn into a tiny but very elaborate 'laboratory' (very different from our own Martian laboratory of years earlier!) and analysed to see if there were any trace of living organisms. The results were somewhat confusing, but it is fair to say that up to now we have no proof that Mars today is anything but sterile. You and I certainly could not survive there; the temperatures are far too low, and the

▲ *During the Viking missions to Mars; from the left, Dr Geoffrey Eglinton (the 'Egg' of the Ag and Egg show), Dr Garry Hunt and me.*

▶ *Impression of the Viking Lander on Mars*

thin carbon-dioxide atmosphere would be quite useless to us.

On the other hand, can we ever hope to build bases on Mars which would allow us to colonize the planet, at least to a limited extent? One man who believed so was Wernher von Braun, who joined me for a *Sky at Night* programme some time before the Viking missions. Von Braun, of course, was the main designer of the V2 rockets, built by the Nazis at Peenemünde, an island in the Baltic, and used to bombard London during the final stages of the war. In 1943 we bombed Peenemünde. I was not on that raid, though I might have been; it was therefore significant that a few years later Wernher von Braun should be having dinner with me in New York. We were on the best of terms, and remained so until, sadly, he died of cancer.

Von Braun was confident that a Martian base would become a practical possibility within a hundred years, probably sooner. This was also the view of Arthur C. Clarke, whom I have known since we were in our teens and who has attained an unique position in science fiction and film production. I remember an early programme in which he predicted the arrival of men on the Moon before 1970. At that period I was sceptical, but in the event he was right and I was wrong.

One other programme of the 1960s must, I feel, be mentioned here. This time I was joined by a very close friend of long standing: Michael Bentine. You will certainly know him as a comedian, but you may not know him as a very skilled scientist. We made our entry attired in space-suits, and were flown across the studio on wires. This was in itself a challenge, because I am no lightweight (it was once said that I give every impression of having been somewhat hastily constructed) and just as the cameras went live the wires became entangled, so that Michael and I bounced helplessly around the studio trying to stabilize ourselves.

Much later, after the Viking landings on Mars, we presented a programme from my study in Selsey. We talked about the usual things — life-forms elsewhere, possibilities of interstellar travel, even flying saucers — and then went into the grand finale. The plan was to see a UFO landing outside my study window, so that Michael and I could be spirited away. To add a touch of realism we filled the room with artificial fog, but we overdid it, and were completely hidden from view as well as being half choked. It took several rehearsals to bring the situation under control.

So far there is not much to be added. I admit, though, that I would dearly like to interview a genuine visitor from Outer Space. If you happen to come across a grounded Saucer, and can locate the pilot, do please persuade him to give me a telephone call.

▲ *Wernher von Braun, the German rocket pioneer who tried to bomb England with V.2s and then master-minded the early American space programme. Despite our differences of the 1940s, we came to be on the best of terms!*

▼ *Do you recognize the two space-men in the studio? They are myself (left) and Michael Bentine (right). We had just descended having been flown around on wires (thick wires in my case).*

19
The League of Planets

▲ *With Dr Lubos Kohoutek at Hamburg Observatory in 1973, when I went there to talk to him about his comet. The fact that the comet failed to become bright was not Dr Kohoutek's fault!*

▲ *Kohoutek's Comet, photographed from Kitt Peak. The comet is evident enough, but is certainly not brilliant. From England it was not really easy to see without optical aid except under extremely good conditions. It may take a better showing when it comes back in around 76,000 years.*

During the 1970s events were moving very quickly indeed, and we did our best to keep pace with them. One thing we had to do was to alter our opening sequence. We had been in the habit of using a lovely old seventeenth-century orrery that I had bought for five shillings well before the war, and which suited our purpose very well. An orrery is in effect a moving model of the Solar System; twist a handle, and the planets will move round at their correct relative speeds. My orrery was beautifully painted, and made a very majestic and spectacular start to our programmes.

Then the Two Ronnies, Ronnie Barker and Ronnie Corbett, elected to do a 'cod' *Sky at Night*. They began with a version of an orrery, and during their opening sequence it naturally came to bits. After that we couldn't use mine again!

We had various successes, and various failures, not all of which were of our making. There was for example Kohoutek's Comet, discovered in 1973 by the Czech astronomer of that name when it was well beyond the orbit of Jupiter, and showed signs of becoming really brilliant. I even flew to Hamburg, where Dr Kohoutek worked, to interview him about it. The Press became excited at the prospect of an imposing cosmic visitor, and so did the end-of-the-world enthusiasts. During one programme I showed a lurid pamphlet written by a Mr Moses David, in which it was claimed that the comet was a sign of Divine Vengeance and would produce storms, tempests, earthquakes and deadly plagues, as well as foretelling the downfall of fascist America and its new Nazi Emperor. However, Kohoutek's Comet proved to be a disappointment, and instead of becoming bright enough to be seen in broad daylight, as some past comets have done, it was barely visible with the naked eye even under good conditions. Mr David must have been somewhat chagrined.

There was, however, another scare of much the same type which was far more widespread and became a thorough nuisance, particularly since it had been put out as a genuinely scientific theory. I was more or less forced into presenting a programme about it, though I ignored it for as long as I could. It involved what became commonly known as the Jupiter Effect.

I first heard about it in 1974, when a book of that title was published by John Gribbin, a writer on the staff of the magazine *New Scientist*, and his colleague Stephen Plagemann. I was sent the book for review, and at first it struck me as being merely funny. It predicted a depressing sequence of events due in the near future, caused by a lining-up of all the planets in a manner which would have dire effects on the Earth, but I dismissed it in a three-line review and thought no more about it.

I had miscalculated. The book was persuasively written, and

it caught the public fancy. Before long observatories were being bombarded with anxious inquiries, and my own postbag swelled at an alarming rate. Things were made no better by a display at the London Planetarium, entitled 'Omens', which treated the affair seriously, causing real misgivings among both adults and children who went to see it. I persuaded the Planetarium authorities to take if off, but it was rather a case of bolting the stable door after the horse had made its escape. After a while it became clear that we would have to devote a programme to it, and on 13 December 1978 we did so.

End-of-the-world panics are nothing new, and recur every now and then. Astrologers in particular are very prone to them. (I have often been asked what I think about astrology, and I always reply that it proves only one scientific fact — namely, that 'there's one born every minute'.) Collisions with comets are favourite themes, and of course there are the religious crackpots, who for some reason usually base themselves on the Book of Daniel. However, there was a twentieth-century precedent for the Gribbin theory. It was due to an Italian named Porta, who had settled in America and had worked up a reasonable reputation as a weather-forecaster. In 1919 he announced that the six largest planets would all be pulling in the same direction, so causing 'gigantic lava eruptions, hurricanes, lightning, colossal rains, floods and fearful cold'. He gave the critical date as 17 December, but nothing happened, and Signor Porta faded quietly out of the news headlines.

I was unable to track down the original pamphlet about Porta's 'League of Planets', as he called it, but evidently there were close points of resemblance between it and the Jupiter

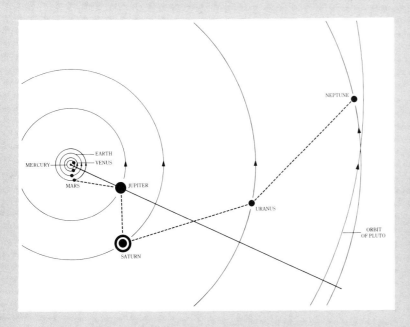

◀ The Jupiter Effect. Actual positions of planets in 1982 showing that they were not in line.

Effect. Gribbin and Plagemann had stated that between 1977 and 1982 all the main planets in the Solar System would be at least approximately aligned, as does indeed happen every 179 years or so. Therefore, they went on, the combined gravitational pulls would stretch out the globe of the Sun; this would cause outbreaks on the solar surface; these outbreaks would eject electrified particles which would bombard the Earth; the Earth's rate of rotation would be altered, increasing the friction between the air and the solid ground; and this would cause strains in the Earth's crust, triggering off major earthquakes. In particular they mentioned the San Francisco area, where a line of weakness (the San Andreas Fault) is indeed liable to produce a strong shock in the foreseeable future, just as it did in 1906 when much of the city was flattened.

The more I looked at these ideas, the more baffled I became. I am no mathematician — before I acquired a pocket calculator my method of totalling up a column of figures was to add from the top downward, then from the bottom upward, and take the average of the two answers — but even I could see that all the planets tugging in the same direction at the same time could have no detectable effect upon the Earth or anything else. The 'tidal stretching' of the Sun could not be more than a millimetre or two, which is not much when we are dealing with a globe 865,000 miles in diameter!

There was also the minor point that no planetary alignment was due between 1977 and 1982. The giant planets were spread out in a curve which, as we have noted, was very useful to the space-planners who wanted to send the same probe from one to the other, but — to take a typical example — the angular separation between two of the giants, Saturn and Neptune, was not far short of a right angle.

I called in Dr Ron Maddison, of Keele University, one of our regular *Sky at Night* guests. He agreed that a programme was desirable, because even after the lapse of several years since the book's publication there was still considerable alarm, not only in Britain but also abroad. The book had appeared in the United States, and even in India, where a guru named B.V. Raman had done his best to reassure his countrymen by claiming that only Los Angeles would be destroyed, not the entire world.

To give the maximum visual effect, we made a recording from my garden in Selsey. We fixed globes on to the ends of poles to represent the various planets, and laid out a kind of Solar System map, though things were complicated by the need to avoid apple-trees which always seemed to be in the most awkward positions possible. We then showed the actual state of affairs during the 'Gribbin period', 1977 to 1982, and showed

figures to illustrate the relative effects of the planets. For example, if we take the Earth's tidal pull on the Sun as unity, that of Neptune works out at 0·0006.

I hoped that our programme would hasten the end of the affair. It had become tedious, and had wasted an enormous amount of time, so that establishments such as the Royal Greenwich Observatory and Jodrell Bank had had hard things to say about it. Again I miscalculated, and the Jupiter Effect took a long time to die. Even in 1983, after the 'critical period' had passed without any natural disasters, the media were still raking it up occasionally. I am glad to say that it seems to have been forgotten now, though I suppose that it may be revived in another 179 years' time.

Of the hundreds of letters I received about it, one stands out in my memory. It came from a viewer in Somerset, in 1981, and was very much of a heart-cry. 'I have decided to give up golf,' he wrote. 'From what astronomers are saying, the world will be destroyed at some time during the next twelve months, and this will give me no time to achieve my ambition of reducing my handicap to single figures. I have therefore given away my clubs, and will play no more.'

Unfortunately, I did not keep the letter; I wish I had, because I would love to know whether he had second thoughts when the world still survived into 1983. If he reads this, I send him my best wishes, coupled with the hope that he has by now got his handicap down to at least scratch.

20
Into the
Black Hole

One result of the change-over from live transmission to recordings is that there is much less chance of disaster. If you make a mistake during a film or a video, you simply go back and do it again. But there was one occasion, in 1978, when I nearly caused a crisis which seems to be remembered even today by certain members of the BBC.

We were to record a perfectly straightforward *Sky at Night*. According to schedule, I would get to Television Centre around 10.30 in the morning; we would rehearse, check all the visuals, have lunch, make the actual recording between 3 and 4 p.m., and then go home. On that particular morning I had a sick headache. There was no obvious reason for it; I had not been out late on the previous night, or anything like that — I simply felt rotten, as everyone does now and then. So before setting out, I decided to take a couple of aspirins, and this was safe enough, because I was not driving my own car, and had been offered a lift from Selsey to Shepherd's Bush.

Unfortunately, I picked up the wrong bottle of tablets, and downed several of what I later found to be my mother's sleeping pills. They took some time to have any effect, but when I went into the studio I was aware of being strangely drowsy, and as soon as I sat down I dropped off. The producer (Patricia Wood) did not know what was the matter, and I was in no position to tell her, because I did not know myself. Luckily, the floor manager was Joan Marsden, known to all and sundry as 'Mother', who summed up the situation quite quickly, and made sure that I was actually awake every time I had to speak to the cameras. By good fortune I was doing the programme on my own, with no guest.

I slumbered peacefully through the lunch-break. We then went into the recording, which was smooth enough because 'Mother' took care to prod me every time my head started to droop. As soon as we had finished I fell asleep, and it was only then that everyone tumbled to the fact that something was definitely awry. Ever since then I have been careful to check that if I take a headache pill, it is not one which will put me out for the count.

'Mother' was involved in another episode, when we were doing a programme about the Great Nebula in Orion. This, as you may or may not know, is a vast cloud of dust and gas inside which fresh stars are being born; it has been aptly described as a stellar nursery, and with the naked eye you can see it quite clearly in the Hunter's Sword, extending away from the three stars of the Belt. It is prominent in the evening sky throughout the whole of winter and spring, and it is always worth looking at. It is well over 1,000 light-years away; the nebular material is being lit up by some very hot stars near its outer edge.

With me was Dr David Allen, of the Siding Spring Observatory in New South Wales. We were discussing the absorption of

▼ *The Great Nebula in Orion, photographed with the Palomar 200-in reflector. The Nebula is a stellar nursery, in which fresh stars are being created out of the tenuous interstellar material; it is over 1000 light-years away.*

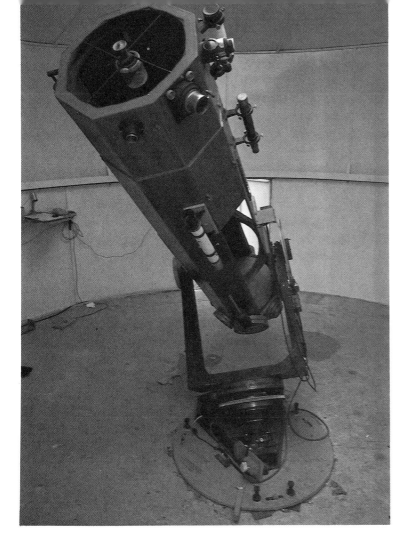

◄ *My 15-in reflector at Selsey, which we have used on many occasions for direct television. It looks antique, with its wooden octagonal 'tube', but is in fact less than twenty years old. I have had it since 1970.*

light in space, and in particular the curious objects which we know to exist deep inside the Nebula. One of these is very powerful in infra-red wavelengths, though we cannot see it in ordinary light because there is too much dust in the way; the situation is rather like that of someone standing in Parliament Square and trying to read the dial of Big Ben through a thick fog. To demonstrate this, we had prepared what amounted to a smoke machine. At a given signal, the machine would blow smoke in front of a large photograph of the Nebula, and hide it.

We tried it out: no problem. Then, in a last rehearsal, the infernal machine went off like a volcano, and 'Mother', who was right in the firing-line, was enveloped in a cloud of oily smoke. What she said was, fortunately, not recorded, but I can assure you that it was very pithy and to the point.

In another programme we took our film unit to my own observatory in Sussex, where the main telescope is a 15-inch reflector, no doubt piffling when compared with the vast instruments in professional establishments but none the less very good. It is housed in a 'dome' which is not graceful and streamlined, but is shaped more like a wedding-cake, with an upper section which revolves on a rail. There is a slit in the roof, so that the telescope inside can be directed to any position in the sky. On the whole, conditions in Selsey are fairly good. I live near the end of the Bill, with sea on three sides, so that there is not much trouble from light-pollution apart from a certain amount of what I call 'Aurora Bognor Regis' in the north. The horizon, too, is satisfactory. Adjoining the dome there was once a tall, stately pear-tree which never produced any pears. One night it got in the way of Saturn, and next morning it turned into a small, stumpy pear-tree. It now yields a pleasing amount of fruit each year; as I have said, it got the message.

Moving the dome round is easy enough, as all that you have to do is to push it from the inside. I was justifiably proud of it, and in this particular programme we set out to show how convenient it was. We set up the cameras, and at the call of 'Action!' I began to push. For once nothing happened, and I shoved and shoved, with nil result. From outside the dome was seen to jerk wildly about; there were odd thumping noises, and eventually the outer flap opened, and my head appeared. 'The flaming thing stuck!'

By good fortune the cameras were still recording. We reshot the sequence correctly, but when we played back the original it struck us as being funny, so at the end of our transmission we put it on the screen as an illustration of an unrehearsed effect.

Exotic objects such as pulsars, quasars and black holes were very much in the news in the 1970s and 1980s, and we devoted several programmes to them. One of these dealt with the centre of the Galaxy, and I was joined by Heather Couper, later to become the first woman President of the British Astronomical Association. I have special memories of this particular programme, because it involved the spectacular disappearance of both Heather and myself into the heart of a black hole.

What exactly is a black hole? Well, it is an area round an old, collapsed star which has shrunk at the end of its brilliant career, and is pulling so strongly that not even light can escape from it. If light cannot break free, then certainly nothing else can, because light is the fastest thing in the universe. There have been suggestions that there may be a massive black hole in the centre of our Galaxy, a region which we cannot see directly because of intervening material, but which we can pinpoint; it lies beyond the lovely star-clouds in the constellation of Sagittarius, the Archer. The Galaxy itself is spiral in form, like a Catherine-wheel, though since we live inside it we cannot see the full effect. Many other galaxies, too, are spiral; photographs taken with large telescopes show them beautifully.

We had the advantage of being in Studio 7, one of the largest in Television Centre, which I knew very well indeed, because all our broadcasts during the Apollo missions had been from it. A large map of the spiral Galaxy had been painted on the floor, with a void in the centre. After we had discussed all the possibilities — which were numerous — we concluded that the central region really was likely to be occupied by a black hole. We then walked across the studio towards it, and by some ingenious camera work we were made to disappear inside it. Not even Paul Daniels could have done better. You will agree, moreover, that shrinking me down to dwarf size takes a great deal of doing!

I wonder whether black holes really exist? Most astronomers believe that they do, but what happens inside them nobody knows, because all the ordinary laws of science break down. I suppose that eventually we will have more positive evidence to guide us, but for the moment black holes remain as mysterious as they are bizarre.

At different times we have also discussed the origin of the universe, which means introducing those strange objects known as quasars — immensely remote, and so luminous that a single quasar can outshine many whole galaxies put together. The present holder of the distance record, a quasar in the dim southern constellation of the Sculptor, was the subject of a programme in September 1986 for which our guest was the Astronomer Royal, Sir Francis Graham-Smith. Unless we have made some fundamental mistake, this quasar is so remote that we are now seeing it not as it is, but as it used to be some 14,000 million years ago. It strains one's imagination, and it is also a fact that every time we present a *Sky at Night* about cosmology I receive stacks of letters, mainly from Biblical Fundamentalists. When asked about how the universe began, I always reply that I have no fixed ideas, because I wasn't there.

I have also worked out a plan for dealing with correspondents of this sort without making them take umbrage. I have three files in my study: one marked 'Letters to be Answered', the second 'Letters to be Answered Some Time', and third 'Oh, my God!' Into the latter go letters from people who could, frankly, be described as nuts. My method is to send the letter from Nut A on to Nut B, merely marked 'For comment'. The two then start writing to each other, and continue to do so ad infinitum. My pinnacle of achievement so far has been to put the International Flat Earth Society in touch with a German organization whose members maintain that the world is hollow, and that we live on the inside of it.

All of which also proves the truth of what I have called Moore's Second Law: 'Every nut thinks that every other nut is a nut!'

National Maritime Museum
Greenwich

National Maritime M
Greenwich

21
Touring
Telescopes

▲ *The third Earl of Rosse ascending the ladder to begin observing with the 72-inch Birr reflector. This is a photograph I took of the lovely painting now hanging in the hall of the Castle.*

▲ *The Rosse 72-inch reflector at Birr Castle, when it was in full working order (around 1850). This is my photograph of a painting now hanging in the hall of the Castle.*

◀ *(previous page) The Lord Mayor's Show, 1984; I was part of the Greenwich float. It was all great fun, and we toured round the City, cheered by the crowds.*

An astronomer without a telescope would be like Hamlet without the Prince, or, for that matter, Tate without Lyle. Inevitably we have concentrated our programmes on telescopes and observatories, and this has involved a good deal of travelling round the world. Yet we began near home, in Southern Ireland.

In 1845 the third Earl of Rosse achieved what had seemed to be an impossibility. Unaided except by workmen from his estate at Birr, in County Offaly, he built what was then much the largest telescope of all time, and used it to make fundamental discoveries; it was he who first saw that some of the so-called starry nebulae are spirals. The telescope was unique, and remains so.

The mirror was no less than 72 inches across. The telescope itself was slung between two massive stone walls, so that it could move only to a limited extent to either side of the north-south line, and one had to wait for the Earth's rotation to bring the target object into view. The third Earl became an expert observer, and was always ready to give help and advice to others. In Birr Castle there is a splendid picture of him climbing the ladder to the telescope eyepiece, and, as always, he is wearing a top-hat.

We first presented a programme from Birr in the early 1960s, when the telescope had been out of use for decades. Since then we have been back there several times, and we will no doubt return before long, because there are great plans afoot for bringing the telescope back into operation; I can hardly wait to look through the eyepiece and see the spiral nebulae just as the third Earl saw them so long ago. Mind you, anyone using the 72-inch has to have a head for heights. One distinguished astronomer of the last century — Dr Romney Robinson, of Armagh — recorded that 'it is rather startling to a person who finds himself suspended over a chasm sixty feet deep, without more than a speculative acquaintance with the properties of trussed beams'.[1]

[1]*Using a modern telescope is less hair-raising, though mishaps can occur. At Siding Spring Observatory, in Australia, you will see a plaque marked 'Gascoigne's Leap', indicating the place where the observer of that name stepped off the main footway round the edge of the inner dome and fell twenty feet on to the observing platform below, fortunately without doing more than sprain his ankle. I have not attempted anything so acrobatic, but when I was once using the main telescope at the Armagh Observatory I managed to get myself jammed half in and half out of the slit in the dome, in the manner of a sweep's brush. This was in the early hours of the morning, so that it was some time before I was rescued.*

This is no place to describe world observatories in detail, so I will confine myself to a few somewhat off-the-record comments which have involved the *Sky at Night*. In 1980, for example, we went to the Lowell Observatory at Flagstaff in Arizona, which of course I knew well. The occasion was the fiftieth anniversary of the discovery of the planet Pluto, by Clyde Tombaugh. In 1930 Clyde was a young amateur; today he is one of America's most senior and respected astronomers. He showed us just how he had conducted the hunt, and we displayed the actual equipment that he had used, including the 13-inch telescope that had been acquired specially for the purpose. Clyde also recalled that on one occasion he came out of the dome in the dead of night (because his programme had been interrupted by clouds) and was aware of what he thought to be a dog walking beside him. It wasn't a dog; it was a prairie wolf.

Subsequently there was a celebration banquet at the University of Las Cruces, where Clyde is now professor emeritus. It was announced that Minor Planet No. 1604 was to be officially named 'Tombaugh' in honour of the occasion — a decision which was previously known to only a few people, including me. Clyde was taken completely by surprise, and commented that at least he now had a piece of real estate that nobody could touch!

(Clyde, I may add, paid me a tremendous compliment when he invited me to collaborate with him on the book *The Planet Pluto*. Later, when the International Astronomical Union decided to name Minor Planet No. 2602 'Moore' in my honour, I appreciated just how he felt at that banquet.)

Arizona is also the home of the Kitt Peak Observatory, which is high up in the mountains and which contains the world's largest telescope designed specifically for studying the Sun. This curious but extremely effective instrument looks more like a scenic railway than a telescope. The sunlight is caught by a huge rotatable mirror and is then directed down an inclined tunnel, where after a series of reflections by other mirrors the beam is brought to focus and the image is studied in an observing room well below ground-level. I also recall the Whipple Observatory, at the summit of another peak, Mount Hopkins. This is a fascinating place — when you get there!

From the foothills of the Santa Rita Mountains you have a clear view of the observatory building, which is perched precariously on the summit of the peak itself and looks like a square hut. To reach it means driving up a partly unmade road which is dangerously narrow, with a sheer rock wall to one side and an equally sheer drop to the other. The last part is so steep that the driver cannot see over the hump. The only method is to accelerate hard, charge up the ramp, and then slam on the

▲ *Clyde Tombaugh, 1980; he looks a little older than he did when he discovered Pluto in 1930, but is just as active. He is standing by the measuring instrument which he used during the successful hunt for Pluto in 1930. We were in the library at the Lowell Observatory, Flagstaff, Arizona.*

▲ *The Lowell 24-in refractor at Flagstaff, Arizona. This was my 1980 picture of it; but during the 1950s and 1960s I used it extensively during my NASA Moon-mapping days.*

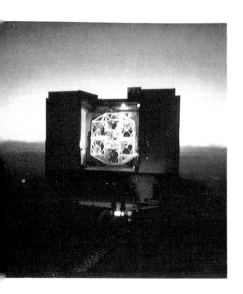

▲ *The heliostat of the Kitt Peak solar telescope; this is the rotatable mirror which catches the sunlight and sends the beam of light down the inclined tunnel.*

▲ *Sunset on the MMT or Multiple Mirror Telescope on Mount Hopkins, Arizona. The six mirrors are shown, together with the rotatable observatory itself.*

brakes to prevent yourself from either crashing into the building or making a rapid descent from the far side of the tiny plateau. Luckily Pieter Morpurgo was driving as well as producing the programme, and it is a tribute to his skill that we arrived in one piece.

The square hut contains a new-generation telescope. It is known as the MMT or Multiple-Mirror Telescope, because instead of using one mirror it has six, each 72 inches in diameter; they work together, so that the light they collect is brought to the same focus, where it can be combined. The MMT is as powerful as a normal telescope with a single 176-inch mirror would be, and there are only two existing instruments larger than that: the 200-inch at Palomar, and the Russian 236-inch which, to be honest, has never worked well.

The whole of the 'hut' covering the MMT turns round, so that there is no need for a rotatable roof. Though the building weighs 500 tons, and turns smoothly, it became stuck on one occasion, and remained so until the cause of the problem was discovered — a dropped screwdriver on the inner rail.

The MMT has cost much less than an equivalent single-mirror telescope would have done. Other instruments of the same type are being planned, and some of these will be set up on the top of Mauna Kea, in Hawaii. We went there during the making of the 25th anniversary *Sky at Night*, mainly to talk about UKIRT, the United Kingdom Infra-Red Telescope, which is the largest of its kind, and has a 150-inch mirror.

Light is a wave motion, and the colour of the light depends

upon its wavelength, from violet (short) to red (long). If the wavelength is longer than that of red light, we come to the infra-red region. Radiations of this sort do not affect our eyes, but you can detect them simply by switching on an electric fire; you will feel the infra-red, in the form of heat, well before the bars have become hot enough to glow.

Astronomers are very interested in infra-red radiation from the sky. Unfortunately, our atmosphere absorbs most of it, water vapour being particularly un-cooperative. The only remedy is to go above the densest and wettest part of the air, so that Mauna Kea, at an altitude of almost 14,000 feet, is a good site. The volcano is, I hope, extinct, but this is not true of its neighbour Mauna Loa, which erupts frequently; indeed once, in the 1880s, its lava reached the outskirts of Hilo, the only sizeable town on the island, and according to tradition was halted at the eleventh hour only by the intervention of a powerful local witch-doctor who had been called in to help.

The only trouble about Mauna Kea is that the rarefied atmosphere means that you are taking in less than 40 per cent of your normal oxygen supply, and some people just cannot tolerate it. Most of our BBC team members were strong, young and athletic, so that doubts were expressed about me, then aged almost sixty and heavily built. In the event I was less affected by the altitude than anyone else, mainly because I am fairly fit but also because as an ex-airman, used to flying about in open cockpits at what seemed in 1940 to be a dizzy height, I knew exactly how to breathe under such conditions.

Hale Pohaku, the 'half-way house', is below 10,000 feet above sea-level, so that few people have breathing problems there. It is the last 4000 feet to the summit which makes all the difference. The road is unmade, but the drive from Hale Pohaku can be done in less than half an hour under normal conditions, though there have been sudden storms which have made the road impassable, and three astronomers were once marooned at the summit for several days — something not to be recommended.

The UKIRT looks like an ordinary telescope, and can in fact be used as such, but its main task is infra-red research, and it has been amazingly successful. Of course, even Mauna Kea is not high enough to provide perfect conditions, but to attain these one needs to use an artificial satellite or a space-station.

There is a strict regulation laying down that only four-wheel-drive vehicles are allowed to use the final stretch between Hale Pohaku and the summit. One distinguished astronomer, however, is not to be daunted, and drives down rather in the manner of a racing demon, skidding round corners, and making the trip at a rate only slightly slower than he would do in free fall. Accepting a lift from him is emphatically not to be recommended for cowards such as me.

If Mauna Kea is the loftiest of the world's major observatories, then certainly Homestake Mine is the lowest. It is in fact a mile below ground, and has been established specially to study the Sun. We went there in the spring of 1982 — it was the last of our recordings for our 25th anniversary — and it was certainly unusual. When I told my friends that I was about to visit Deadwood Gulch, country of the gunslingers, to go down a gold-mine and look at a tank of cleaning-fluid, few of them believed me; but it was perfectly true.

I have already said something about the way in which the Sun shines, producing its energy by changing one gas (hydrogen) into another (helium). During this process it emits numbers of particles known as neutrinos, which have no electrical charge and virtually no mass, so that they are not easy to detect. As you read these lines, you are being penetrated by many neutrinos every second, but please do not worry, because they can do you no harm, and can usually pass unhindered right through the entire globe of the Earth.

Theorists are anxious to know just how many neutrinos the Sun sends out, but how exactly do you catch them? One way is to make them collide with the atoms of chlorine, one of the two elements which makes up common salt (the other is sodium). If a chlorine nucleus is hit by a neutrino it may be transformed into an atom of another kind which is fairly easy to identify.

Dr Raymond Davis, of the Brookhaven National Laboratory in the United States, had a bright idea. Why not produce a large tank of chlorine, expose it to the Sun, and see how many of its atoms are hit by neutrinos? One immediate problem was that chlorine in its normal form is a gas, but it can be combined with other substances to make what it called perchloroethylene, better known as cleaning-fluid. In fact, a tank of cleaning-fluid would serve as a 'neutrino telescope'.

This was not all. There are particles inappropriately known as cosmic rays which come in from space from all directions all the time, and would produce the same effects in the cleaning-fluid. But neutrinos are more penetrative than cosmic rays, so that if the tank were sufficiently shielded then the cosmic rays would be unable to get at it. A mile of rock would do the trick. So the scientists contacted the owners of the Homestake Gold Mine, South Dakota, and met with a favourable response. The mine is still functional, but at a mile below ground there was a disused shaft which would be ideal for the astronomers. A cave was hollowed out, and the tank installed.

Deadwood itself is a fascinating place. It was here, little more than a hundred years ago, that the gunslingers gathered:

Calamity Jane, Wild Bill Hickok, Doc Holliday and the rest. We actually went to the saloon where Wild Bill met his end in 1876, because someone was unfriendly enough to pump bullets into him. Homestake is some miles away, at the town of Lead (pronounced Leed) in the heart of the Black Hills, which belie their name because for much of the year they are snow-covered and brilliant white. It was deep snow when we arrived there, in January 1982, ready to go down the mine.

Dressing-up is an essential preliminary. This involves a hard helmet, safety spectacles, a miner's lamp, and a device known as a self-rescuer. One of the hazards of the mine is that any moment there may be a rush of carbon monoxide, which is both colourless and odourless, but can kill you very quickly if you breathe it in. If there is any sign of danger, an alarm sounds; if you are wise you will unwrap your flask-sized rescuer, put the nozzle in your mouth and hold your nose before breathing. With luck, you can survive in this manner for at least an hour. Another thing to bear in mind is the cable at the top of the tunnel leading to the solar observatory. It is only a few feet above your head as you walk along, but it carries a current of electricity powerful enough to fry you like an egg if you happen to touch it.

We put on our gear, entered the miner's cage and descended, rather bumpily, getting off at the first stop and leaving the miners to go down another mile. The first thing that struck me was the warmth. Above, the temperature was sub-zero; in the tunnel it was at least 80 degrees Fahrenheit, and I gather that in the lower reaches, where gold is still being produced, there is an urgent need for cooling equipment.

We were met by Ray Davis and his colleague, Keith Rowley, who showed us round. The tank holds 100,000 gallons of cleaning fluid, and is flushed out every two months to see how many neutrinos have scored direct bulls'-eyes on the atoms of chlorine; for the rest of the time the observatory can be left unguarded, to operate on its own. The method of carrying out the analyses is highly complex, and I do not propose to describe it here, but the result is that far fewer neutrinos are being detected than ought to be the case. I am quite sure that there is nothing wrong with the experiment (Ray and Keith are much too good to make any mistakes, and anyway the Russians have set up a similar detector with similar results), so either there is an error in our theory, or else there is something abnormal about the Sun's behaviour at the present time. Reducing the estimated temperature of the Sun's core by a million degrees or so would solve the 'neutrino problem', but would raise other difficulties. At the moment we still do not know the answer, but I still smile at the thought that astronomers have had to burrow deep into the ground to carry out this sort of research.

Standing by the Palomar 200-in reflector as we were there making a programme. This programme is still used at the Observatory at the Visitor Centre.

The Yerkes Observatory, as I photographed it in 1986 when we went there for a programme. It is architecturally superb and backs on to a golf-course.

The Yerkes 40-in refractor, as I photographed it in 1986; it is the largest telescope of its kind, and probably will remain so.

At various times we have also been to the other major optical observatories in the United States: Palomar, with its great 200-inch reflector; Mount Wilson, now sadly put into mothballs because of the increased glare from neighbouring Los Angeles; and Yerkes, at Williams Bay not far from Chicago. Yerkes, easily accessible and backing on to a golf-course, is unusual in many ways. Its main telescope is a refractor, which has a 40-inch lens and is the largest of its kind in the world. In 1917 an observer named John Mellish turned it towards Mars, and is said to have seen craters there almost half a century before they were revealed by the Mariner spacecraft. During our visit, in 1986, I was given the opportunity to make an observation with the same telescope, though Mars was then a long way from the Earth and no craters came into view.

The 40-inch was master-minded by George Ellery Hale, an enthusiastic astronomer who also had the happy knack of persuading friendly millionaires to finance his schemes. The 40-inch was funded by a Chicago businessman named Charles T. Yerkes — hence the Observatory's name. The building itself is a splendid piece of architecture, but just before the official opening one of the trustees noticed that the columns outside the main entrance included representations of a bee about to sting a man on the nose. Most undignified — and, moreover, could it symbolize Yerkes being stung for the money? A stone-mason was summoned, and painstakingly chiselled off ninety-six bees. You can still the scars where the unwelcome insects used to be.

I also heard another story about Yerkes, concerning the second director, Edwin Frost. For some reason or other he wanted to be able to tell the temperature without using a thermometer, and he devised a novel way of doing it. For part of the year crickets are very much in evidence around the Observatory; Frost found that if you count the number of chirps made by a cricket in thirteen seconds and then add 40, you will have the temperature in degrees Fahrenheit. I have been

The Isaac Newton Telescope, as I photographed it during our first programme from La Palma. Its new mirror is just over 100 inches in diameter: the old mirror, in use during the telescope's spell at Herstmonceux, was a 98-in.

▼ With Sir Bernard Lovell at Jodrell Bank in 1981, when we gave our tribute to him in The Sky at Night on his retirement. The great 250-ft dish for which he was responsible is in the background.

▼ Celebrations at the centenary of GMT, in 1984. The stamp is a little big to put on a letter; the Old Royal Observatory shows up well in the background.

longing to try it out for myself, but during my visits to Yerkes it has always been the close season for crickets.

Please do not think that we have ignored British observatories: far from it. We have presented quite a number of programmes from Herstmonceux Castle, which has been the home of the Royal Greenwich Observatory but is now under threat of closure for reasons which seem as damaging as they are illogical. We have also been to La Palma, in the Canary Islands, where our largest telescopes have been erected, and to Jodrell Bank in Cheshire, home of the famous 250-foot radio telescope. When Professor Sir Bernard Lovell officially retired, in 1981, we devoted a programme to his achievements — which, believe me, are considerable by any standards. Without him, radio astronomy would not today be the powerful force that it actually is.

Finally, what about Greenwich itself, the Old Royal Observatory in the park? We went there in October 1984, exactly a hundred years after Greenwich Time had been adopted as the standard for the whole world, a move opposed by only a few countries (one of which was, of course, France). I have graphic memories of wading through a pond in the Park which is bisected by the prime meridian, the line which divides the Earth into its eastern and western hemispheres. This was also the only time I have taken part in the Lord Mayor's Show, as I was part of the Greenwich float. Driven around the streets of London, greeted by cheering crowds, I felt truly regal.

Obviously we will continue to visit the world's great observatories in future editions of The Sky at Night. I particularly want to go back to Siding Spring in New South Wales, not only to see the superb telescopes there but also to return to the Warrumbungle National Park and make friends with the local kangaroos. I am also determined to go back to Yerkes at a suitable time of the year; I will never rest until I have found out whether Edwin Frost was right about those chirping crickets.

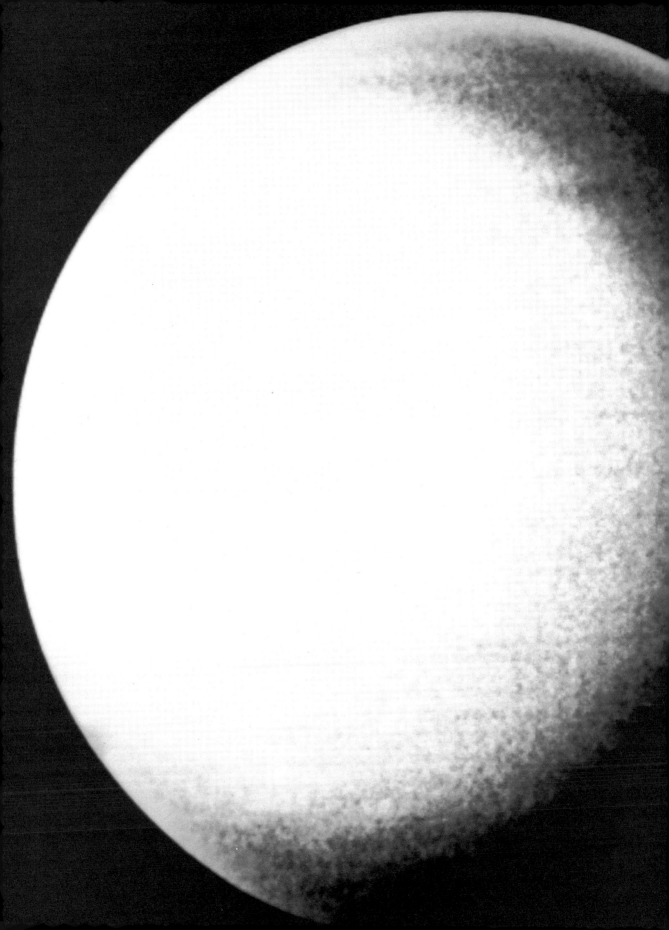

22
The Tilted Giant

Two major events dominated the *Sky at Night* planning during early 1986. The mission to Halley's Comet was due in March. Before that, in January, Voyager 2 was scheduled to by-pass the strange green planet Uranus, and send back information from the depths of the Solar System.

Voyager 2, that cosmic snooker-ball, had already encountered both Jupiter and Saturn, following in the path of its predecessor Voyager 1. From the Jet Propulsion Laboratory at Pasadena, in California, we had presented programmes each time, and we had no intention of being left out of the third lap of the journey. So we departed once more, ready for anything which might eventuate.

The earlier missions had been eventful by any standards. Jupiter had shown its mass of detail, but even more intriguing had been the main satellites, which turned out to be bizarre worlds. The two outermost, Ganymede and Callisto, were predictably icy and cratered, but Europa was as smooth as a billiard ball, and Io, slightly larger than our Moon, was both red and volcanic, with a sulphur-coated surface. Tremendous eruptions were going on constantly, and since Io is immersed in Jupiter's lethal radiation zone it must be the most unwelcoming world in the entire Solar System. Go there by all means if you like, but don't expect me to come with you.

Saturn too had provided its quota of surprises. The ring system was much more complicated than had been expected, and there were thousands of narrow ringlets and minor divisions; when I first saw them I thought that we must be dealing with some sort of 'wave phenomenon' due to the gravitational pulls of Saturn's satellites, and it now seems that I may well have been right. Of the satellites themselves the most interesting, if the least spectacular, was Titan, which we already knew to be surrounded by a cloudy atmosphere. Before the encounter Garry Hunt and I were arguing as to whether we would be able to see through to the actual surface. I thought we would; Garry thought we wouldn't, and he proved to be right. The atmosphere turned out to be made up chiefly of nitrogen, with quantities of methane. What the surface conditions are like we do not yet know; there could be cliffs of solid methane, rivers of liquid methane, and a methane rain dripping down from the orange clouds above.

As it drew away from Saturn, Voyager 2 developed a fault. The platform carrying the cameras jammed, and for a while the NASA planners feared the worst, particularly as Voyager 1 had completed its task and was not directed towards either of the outer giant planets. Luckily the fault corrected itself, more or less, and all was set for the encounter with Uranus in 1986.

Uranus had been discovered by William Herschel in 1781. At

▼ William Herschel, discoverer of Uranus. This is a portrait, as Herschel died in 1822 before photography came along, but it is certainly a good likeness.

that time Herschel was living in the city of Bath, where he was a professional organist at the Octagon Chapel; his home was 19 New King Street, which was in danger of demolition two centuries later before the Herschel Society stepped in and saved it. (Do visit it next time you are in Bath. We have converted it into a small but interesting museum, abounding in Herscheliana.) Later in his career Herschel moved to Slough, where he set up what was then the largest telescope ever made, a reflector with a 49-inch mirror which was not surpassed until the completion of Lord Rosse's remarkable 72-inch in 1845. Observatory House, Slough, was pulled down in 1960; I took some of the very last pictures of it. The place where the 49-inch once stood is now the courtyard of the Rank Xerox works, and is marked by a monument which I once likened to a cheese-manufacturer's nightmare.

Uranus proved to be a giant world, around 30,000 miles in diameter, moving round the Sun far beyond the path of Saturn, and taking 84 years to complete one revolution. Telescopically, it shows up as a pale, featureless greenish disc. With the naked eye it can just be seen if you know where to look for it, but I am not surprised that it escaped detection before Herschel happened upon it during one of his routine 'surveys of the heavens'.

▲ *The garden of 19 New King Street, Bath. This is where William Herschel may have stood when he discovered Uranus in 1781. When the Herschel Society took over No. 19 the house was dilapidated and the garden a wilderness — things now are very different!*

◄ *Replica of the telescope used by Herschel to discover Uranus, in 1781. This replica was made by Michael Tabb for the Herschel Museum in 1980.*

Like Jupiter and Saturn, Uranus has a gaseous surface, but it contains more water and ammonia than either of the larger giants. Its axis is unique in being tipped over, so to speak, with the result that day and night conditions there are most peculiar. Each pole has a period of sunlight equal to 21 Earth-years, with a corresponding period of darkness at the opposite pole; there are times, as in the mid-1980s, when one pole is turned directly towards the Sun and the Earth, so that to us it appears to be in the centre of the planet's disc. There were five satellites known before the Voyager mission, all of which are smaller than our Moon, and it was also known that Uranus has a system of thin, dark rings which are quite unlike the glorious rings of Saturn.

Apart from this, our knowledge was frankly meagre, which is why there was so much interest in the Voyager flight. We also knew that it was likely to be the last Uranus probe for many years.

As soon as we reached JPL we worked out our schedule, and then began some preliminary filming. A full-scale model of Voyager, in the main auditorium, was very useful; we were able to show and describe the main features of it, including the scan platform which had caused so much trouble. Power came from a small on-board nuclear generator, since solar power could not be used at the vast distance of Uranus — over 1780 million miles from the Sun.

We were also able to film in the DSN or Deep Space Network, which has been in use for twenty-four hours a day ever since the flight of the first planetary probe, Mariner 2 to Venus in 1962. This is really impressive. The DSN is quiet; there are screens and control desks everywhere, and it all seems most futuristic. One almost expects Professor Quatermass to walk in at any moment.

I think that the excitement at JPL was greater than at the times of the Jupiter and Saturn missions. Then, at least, we had some idea of what to expect; with Uranus we didn't. How long was the planet's rotation period? Was there a magnetic field? Would Uranus send out radio waves, and what was the cause of the extraordinary axial tilt? We hoped that the coming week would provide us with at least some of the answers.

We were not disappointed. The first major discovery was that of a whole swarm of new satellites, not far outside the limits of the rings; indeed, one of the newcomers was actually immersed in the ring-system. All were small, but they had not been expected, and they were most interesting. One NASA scientist commented that it seemed as though some outside agency had literally peppered the neighbourhood of Uranus with moonlets.

The next revelation was that Uranus was indeed a radio

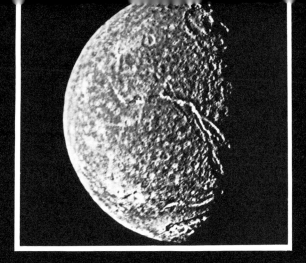

◀ *Titania. The highest-resolution picture of Titania from Voyager 2, taken from 229,000 miles. The resolution is down to 8 miles. Note the immense valley of Messina Chasmata, extending down to the middle of the terminator.*

source, and had a strong magnetic field, with the magnetic poles some 60 degrees away from the poles of rotation — another new departure in the Solar System. To confuse matters still further, the south pole of rotation, which is at present facing the Sun, is closer to the *north* magnetic pole. A strange 'electro-glow' was found in the Uranian atmosphere, and several new rings were identified, one of which extends downward to within a few thousand miles of the cloud-tops. The Uranian 'day' proved to be just over 17 hours long.

We had hoped to see surface features, basically similar to those of Jupiter and Saturn, but all that could be made out were vague clouds, so that Uranus is a relatively bland world. However, we saw striking details on the larger satellites. Of these, three (Ariel, Titania and Oberon) were ice-coated and cratered, but they were not alike; Oberon has dark-floored enclosures, while Ariel exhibits broad valleys which look as though they must have been cut by some liquid, presumably water, in far-off times. The other main satellite, Umbriel, has a much darker surface, with subdued craters, giving the impression of being exceptionally ancient. Nothing can have happened on Umbriel for thousands of millions of years in the past.

Finally there was the innermost of the previously known satellites, Miranda, which had been discovered by Gerard Kuiper in 1948. It is no more than about 300 miles across, but it has an amazingly varied surface, with towering ice-cliffs, craters, valleys, and strange enclosures which looked like race-tracks. 'You name it, Miranda has it,' was one of my comments during our programme. Just why Miranda has this sort of landscape is something else which we do not yet know.

For once in a way, there were no untoward incidents during our programme-making, and we left JPL well satisfied. Meanwhile, it is worth noting that after a journey of so many millions of miles, lasting for over eight years, Voyager 2 reached its closest point to Uranus precisely one minute nine seconds early. British Rail, please copy.

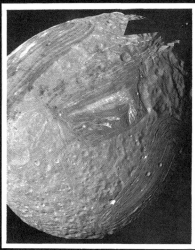

▲ *Miranda, showing the 'race-track' — Elsinore Corona; I am sure that Hamlet would have been as puzzled by it as I am. Miranda shows the most incredibly varied landscape known.*

179

23
The Year of the Comet

Of all the comets in the sky
There's none like Comet Halley
We see it with the naked eye,
And periodically.

Hardly Shakespearian (or even Baconian) verse, but it sums up the popular view of Halley's Comet, much the most famous of all our cosmic visitors. It returns at intervals of approximately 76 years; it was back in 1910, and was again due to pass its perihelion, or closest point to the Sun, in February 1986. Everybody was waiting for it, and this applied most forcibly to *The Sky at Night*.

There had been a lengthy build-up. I am myself a founder member of the Halley's Comet Society, which had been masterminded by Brian Harpur in the mid-1970s. We have our own special tie, with a 1986 motif,[1] and we are, we feel, unique inasmuch as the Society has no aims, objects or ambitions, and does nothing except meet periodically on licensed premises. (One such gathering was held in the Long Room at Lord's; I think I was about the only regular cricketer present.) It has even been said that the Society is the only completely useless organization in the world apart, of course, from the United Nations.

What of Edmond Halley himself? He must have been a great character; the story of how he once pushed the Tsar of Russia through a hedge in a wheelbarrow seems to be well authenticated (let me stress that it was the Tsar who was in the wheelbarrow, not the hedge). One of his few enemies, the puritanical Rev. John Flamsteed, commented acidly that Halley drank brandy and swore like a sea-captain, which he probably did. But he was also a great scientist, and it was he who persuaded Isaac Newton to write the immortal book about gravitation, for which, incidentally, Halley paid out of his own pocket. Later he succeeded Flamsteed as Astronomer Royal at Greenwich. Unfortunately I never met him — he died in 1742, which was a little before my time — but at least I have been photographed alongside the model of him now in Madame Tussaud's. The picture is reproduced here. (Halley is on the left.)

▲ *Edmond Halley. Unfortunately I never met him — he died in 1742, a little before my time — so the next best thing is to be photographed beside him. This was actually taken in a BBC studio in 1986; model by courtesy of Madame Tussaud's!*

[1] *We have now altered this to a 2061 design, to mark the next return of the comet. At our meeting on 13 November 1986, following an impressive ceremony in which a Halley plaque was unveiled in Westminster Abbey, Eamonn Andrews turned up wearing the first of the new ties — a classic piece of one-upmanship.*

◄ *Halley's Comet as it was on 12 May 1910, as photographed from Yerkes Observatory, near Chicago. The tail then extended to 30°. The blob to the right is the planet Venus. Would that the last return had been as favourable!*

Halley observed a bright comet in 1682. At that time nobody was sure how these wraithlike objects moved; even Newton thought that they travelled in straight lines, by-passing the Sun only once before departing for ever. Halley was not so confident. He found that the 1682 comet moved in the same way as comets previously seen in 1607 and 1531, and he was bold enough to forecast that the three were one and the same, in which case it would return once more in 1758. It did, and again in 1835 and 1910. We looked forward to welcoming it anew.

There was one disadvantage. In 1910, and at many previous returns, the comet had been a prominent naked-eye object, and old records say that in the year 837 it had been brilliant enough to cast shadows. In 1986, however, the Earth and the comet were in the wrong places at the wrong times, and at perihelion the comet would be almost behind the Sun in the sky, so that it would be out of view altogether. Nothing could be done about it; we had to make the best of a bad job. It would at least be visible without optical aid for some months before and after perihelion, though when at its best, in March and April 1986, it would be too far south in the sky to rise over any part of Britain.

We planned our programmes as early as 1981. Then, on 16 October 1982, three astronomers using the 200-inch reflector at Palomar in California detected the comet as a tiny speck, so faint that only the world's largest telescope, combined with modern electronic equipment, had any chance of showing it.

I heard about the discovery a few hours after it had been made, and I made a series of telephone calls to America, making contact with one of the discoverers, David Jewitt, whom I knew. Hastily we prepared a programme, persuaded the BBC to give us a ten-minute slot just before midnight, and put on a *Sky at Night* 'special' which included a phone interview with David Jewitt. The stage was set.

Incidentally, this was about the only time when we ended our transmission with unfamiliar music. Instead of 'At the Castle Gate', we used the march *Halley's Comet*, which I had written for the Society and which had been recorded by the Band of the Royal Transport Corps. I am proud to add that they now use my march quite regularly in their ceremonies!

There were the usual noises from the prophets of doom, who regarded Halley as an agent of divine displeasure, and the end of the world was routinely predicted, so that at one of our Society meetings we were greeted with demonstrators wielding placards. Yet for a long time the comet remained well beyond the range of most observers, either professional or amateur. With my own 15-inch reflector I did not have my first view of it until September 1985, when it was still no more than a tiny fuzz against the background of stars, but then it started to brighten, and to develop a tail.

During the autumn and winter of 1985 the comet became more accessible, but the weather over Britain was perverse and clouds covered the sky for weeks on end. It was quite infuriating, and I had numerous letters from people, who wanted to know just when they might expect to get a decent view. A few were lucky, of course; I had a request from a 96-year-old who had seen the comet in 1910 and was anxious to see it again, and I am glad to say that when she was brought to my observatory she was rewarded with an excellent sighting. To the general public, however, Halley was proving to be a non-event. At one stage I acted as a guide during specially arranged aircraft flights, sent up to beat the clouds, and although comet-spotting through the window of a Jumbo jet is not exactly easy it was better than nothing. I recall one anxious passenger who asked me whether it was really safe to go up to a height of 35,000 feet; would we be in any danger of colliding with our target? I hope I was able to reassure him.

By then, several spacecraft were already on their way, and one of Man's most ambitious experiments had started.

In 1910 the very idea of sending up a rocket to rendezvous with a comet (or anything else) was still ludicrous enough to make the average scientist scream with laughter. By 1985 things had changed, and a cometary mission was almost inevitable. The Americans had planned an extensive programme, but then abandoned it because of the cost — for which they will certainly kick themselves for the next 76 years. The

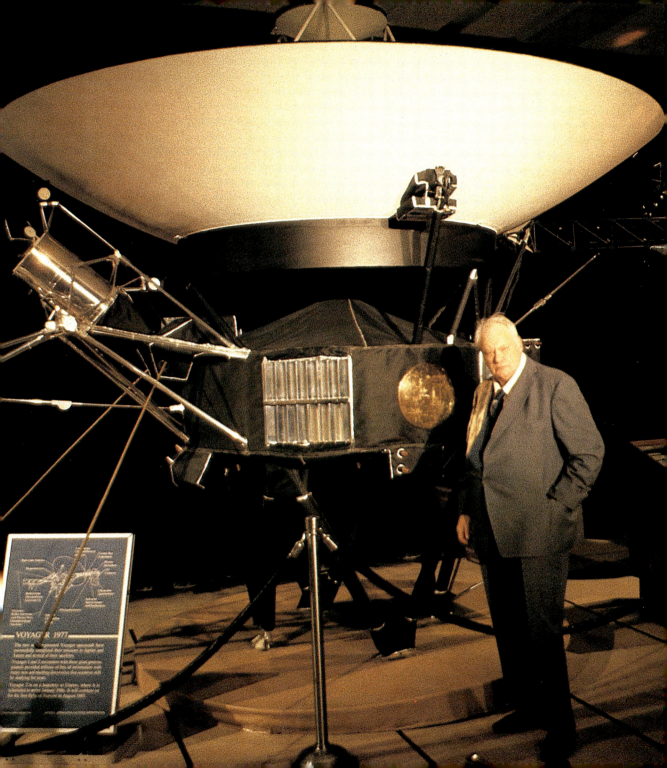

▲ *The DSN or Deep Space Network at the Jet Propulsion Laboratory, as I photographed it during the Voyager 2 passing of Uranus. It is really futuristic, and most impressive.*

▶ *Saturn's rings, from Voyager;*
instead of being straightforward,
there are thousands of 'ripples', due
possibly to eave effects caused by the
pulls of Saturn's satellites.

The four Galilean satellites of Jupiter: icy and cratered Callisto (1) and Ganymede (2), smooth Europa (3), and the red, volcanic Io (4), which is possibly the most lethal world known to us. These are, of course, Voyager pictures.

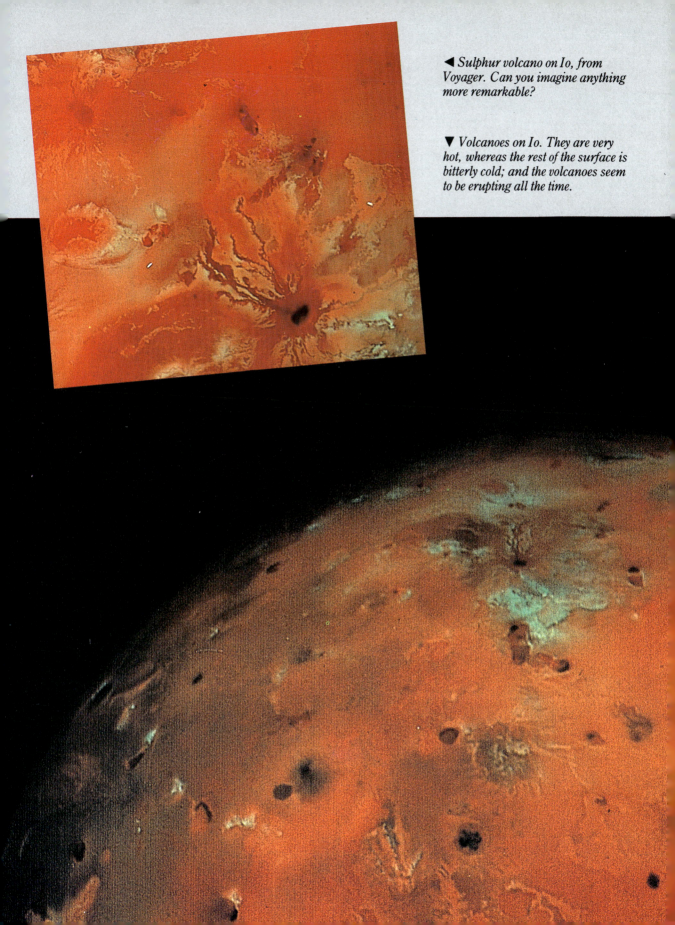

◄ *Sulphur volcano on Io, from Voyager. Can you imagine anything more remarkable?*

▼ *Volcanoes on Io. They are very hot, whereas the rest of the surface is bitterly cold; and the volcanoes seem to be erupting all the time.*

Ganymede, Jupiter's third and largest satellite. It has an icy, cratered surface, as shown in this Voyager picture. The dark oval area is called Galileo Regio.

responsibility devolved upon the Japanese (two small probes, costing about ten yen each), the Russians (two 'Vega' craft, which were to go to the comet by way of Venus) and the European Space Agency team, with a space-probe named Giotto in honour of the Florentine artist who had painted the comet several centuries earlier and used it as a model for the Star of Bethlehem in his picture *The Adoration of the Magi*.[2] Of these, only Giotto was scheduled to go right into the comet's head and send back information from point-blank range.

Giotto was built by British Aerospace in Bristol, and we went there to film it. It was quite sobering; this modest vehicle, crammed with instruments, was to carry out a survey of an entirely new type. I dressed up in a white coat, not for effect but to guard against bringing dust into the 'clean room', and interviewed some of those who had been responsible for the design and the actual building. Then, on 1 July 1985, British Aerospace invited me to watch the actual launching, which took place from the rocket base at Kourou, in French Guyana.

Kourou, French-built and run, is very close to the equator, and is within range of the once-notorious Devil's Island; I am told that one of the ex-convicts now owns a restaurant in the town. The climate is frankly awful. The heat is intense, day and night, and the atmosphere is dripping wet, while even the rain is hot. Against this, the location is ideal for rocket launchings, and the base itself is reassuringly modern.

There could be only one chance, because there was only one Giotto. Ariane, the rocket used for the launch, does not have an untarnished record, and has been known to dump satellites and space-probes in the sea, so that we were all decidedly apprehensive. Mercifully, this particular Ariane worked faultlessly, and we cheered with all our might as soon as we knew that Giotto was safely on its way. The date of encounter was to be 13 March 1986, after a journey of over 420,000,000 miles.

Shortly before that, the two Japanese and the two Russian vehicles would have passed by the comet, keeping clear of the main head, and we were assured that all available information would be sent straight on to the European headquarters at Darmstadt, in West Germany, so that if need be Giotto could be re-targeted at the latest possible moment. This is exactly what happened. There are no iron curtains or even bamboo curtains in astronomy, and the Halley saga provided a superb example of full international collaboration.

▲ *Model of Giotto at Darmstadt, March 1986, during the actual mission. I am standing by it to show that it is not really very large!*

[2] *I can assure you that Halley's Comet was not the Star of Bethlehem; it returned years before the birth of Christ.*

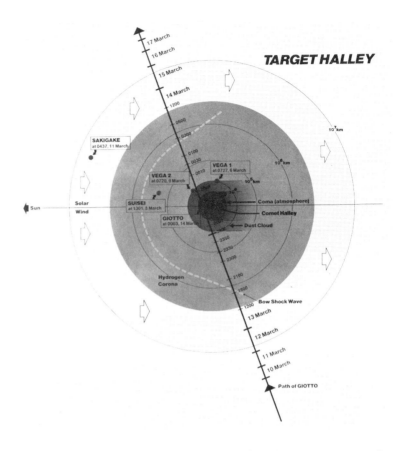

▶ Progress of the space-probes through Halley's Comet; two Japanese (Sakigake, Suisei): two Russians (the Vegas) and ours (Giotto). All were successful, but we may do even better in 2061.

▼ Jan Oort (right) and Fred Whipple, with me at the Giotto programme from Darmstadt — they are the best-known 'comet specialists' of our time.

We planned to cover the mission 'live', which meant transmitting through midnight: the ESA team, led by Dr Rüdeger Reinhard, was quite happy about this, and promised us full facilities. I wanted to present the entire programme from Darmstadt, but *The Sky at Night* does not have that kind of budget, so the *Horizon* programme joined in and put on commentaries from the Old Royal Observatory in Greenwich Park with which I had nothing to do.

Most of us expected the comet to show an icy nucleus, a few miles in diameter, from which jets would be spurting out; almost the only dissentients were Sir Fred Hoyle and his colleague Chandra Wickramasinghe, who believed that the nucleus would be dark. The main danger to Giotto would come from dust, which is very plentiful in the neighbourhood of any large comet. Though the individual particles are tiny, they would meet Giotto at a relative speed of over 40 miles per second, so that they would have tremendous penetrating power and would be a severe test even for the ingenious double shield which had been designed by Dr Fred Whipple. Few people expected Giotto to survive its perilous journey, but we hoped that it would survive for long enough to send back data from near the nucleus.

The organization at Darmstadt was totally different from that at NASA. After all, the Americans were used to this sort of situation, with an invasion by television crews and journalists as well as visiting scientists, but the Germans weren't, and at first they did not know just how to handle it. So far as we were concerned they did their best, and provided a small room which we could fit up as a studio with just enough room for the director, the camera-man, the sound recordist, a guest and Me. We had to contact our interviewees by sending messengers, because the telephone lines were usually jammed, and it was all somewhat chaotic, though it improved as the mission progressed. Frankly, the fact that I knew all the leading experts was a great help, and guests came and went regularly, among them Fred Whipple (originator of the 'dirty iceball' theory of comets) and Jan Oort (who was the world's leading authority on cometary origin). Rüdeger Reinhard took time off to join us, and so did many others, including members of the actual Giotto imaging team.

By the time we went on the air we already knew that the Japanese and the Russians had filled their rôles nobly, but in the programme itself we had to improvise, and to be honest things were not made easier by the fact that at times we had to leave Darmstadt and go over to the *Horizon* programme at Greenwich, but it soon became evident that there was a great deal to be said. The pictures from Giotto were of the false colour variety — that is to say, modified so as to make scientific analysis easier — but they were distinct enough, and were certainly spectacular.

As Giotto sped in towards the nucleus, the signals were strong. Then, just before the moment of closest approach, they faded. Had the probe been destroyed? No; what had happened was that it had been hit by a particle about the size of a rice-grain, and the main transmitting aerial had been jolted out of alignment. While we were still broadcasting, the signals were picked up again, though by then Giotto was already on its outward journey from the comet's nucleus.

By the time we ended our programme we were able to give the preliminary results. As Hoyle and Wickramasinghe had forecast, the nucleus was dark, and Dr Keller, head of the Giotto camera team, described it as 'blacker than velvet', so that Fred Whipple's dirty ice-ball turned out to have more dirt than had been expected. The nucleus was about 7½ miles long by 5 miles broad, and was shaped rather like a potato.

The temporary fading of the signals happened when the spacecraft hit what can only be described as a dust-storm close to the comet's nucleus, but at least Giotto survived, even though the camera was put out of action. It is now on its way back to the neighbourhood of the Earth, and if it is still sufficiently operational it may even be sent on to rendezvous with another comet. Certainly it has been an outstanding success.

We in the *Sky at Night* were not yet finished with Halley. The best viewing time was expected to be in March and April 1986, from the southern hemisphere, and I joined the party which the Explorers Travel Club was sending to Australia. I planned to photograph the comet as often as I could, and use the pictures in a later programme when we had had time to pull all the results together.

Our party was about forty strong. We landed at Sydney, and then drove across to Siding Spring, where, as I have said, there is one of the world's greatest observatories. I then had to fly back to Sydney to made a broadcast, while the rest of the party drove by coach to Alice Springs in the very centre of the Australian continent. Having made my broadcast, I flew on to Alice Springs, reaching it on 11 April ahead of the other members of the group.

Bear in mind that Alice Springs is one of the driest places in Australia. Before I arrived there, there had been no appreciable rainfall for five years, and none at all for the previous eight months. Yet the instant I touched down at the airport, the heavens opened. The local Pressmen were quick to blame me, and solemnly photographed me as I shielded myself beneath an umbrella which had been rooted out of store specially for the purpose!

► *When I reached Alice Springs, rain fell for the first time in many moons. The Press somehow found an umbrella, and took this picture of me as I protested volubly to the rain-gods.*

▲ *Halley's Comet, 13 December 1985.*

The rain soon cleared, and the comet shone forth. By now it was nearing the constellation of the Centaur, which is too far south to be seen from England, and it was quite unmistakable. Together with Douglas Arnold, who is (unlike me) an expert photographer, I drove out into the desert to get as far away from any town lights as possible. We were not alone, because several of the local astronomers accompanied us and acted as guides, but our trip was not uneventful. When we were unwise enough to leave the main road and take to an unmade track, we became acutely aware that the wheels of our car were sinking into the deep red dust, and it took several hours to extricate ourselves.

Following an inspection of Ayers Rock, a huge block which rises from the desert for no apparent reason, we set off in the direction of Darwin, camping at various overnight sites. It was on 17 April, near Tennant's Creek, that I had an odd experience. By about four o'clock in the morning the comet had dropped so low in the sky that no further photography was possible, and I decided to get some sleep, so I went into my tent and undressed. Suddenly the flap opened, and in came — a wallaby which wanted a drink! I gave it two cupfuls of water, which it swallowed happily and then withdrew. (This is not such a tall story as it may sound. We were on an official camping site, and the wallaby was quite used to human company, so that one could go up to it at any time and tickle its ears.)

By then the comet was in Centaurus, and people kept on coming up to me to say that 'they could see two comets'. The second object was not in fact a comet at all, but a globular cluster, Omega Centauri, made up of about a million stars, and so far away that its light takes thousands of years to reach us. Still, I must admit that superficially the two looked very alike, and for a while they were in the same binocular field.

I came back by way of Bali, in Indonesia. On 24 April there was a total eclipse of the Moon, and for more than an hour the sky darkened, so that the comet could be seen with the naked eye for the very last time. It was an unforgettable sight, particularly in that romantic setting.

Our final Halley programme was transmitted in October 1986, by which time the comet was a thing of the past so far as most people were concerned even though giant telescopes will enable it to be followed for some years yet. It will be back in the year 2061. I am not likely to see it myself, unless I live to the unusual age of a hundred and thirty-eight, but no doubt there will be full *Sky at Night* coverage, and perhaps my successor of that period will even be able to carry out a live broadcast while standing on the velvet-black nucleus. Time will tell.

I have already quoted a famous rhyme about Halley's Comet.

Let me end with another. In the Halley's Comet Society we insist on pronouncing the name to rhyme with 'crawley' rather than 'tally', because apparently that is how Edmond himself actually said it. Because the 1986 return was so unfavourable, my colleague Dr John Mason produced the following variation:

> Of all the comets in the sky
> There's none like Comet Hawley.
> We saw it with the naked eye
> But this time, rather poorly!

Just in case you hope for a better view in 2061, I must point out that conditions will, if possible, be even worse than they were in 1986. Look out for the comet by all means, but don't say that you haven't been warned.

▼ *Preparing to open a bottle of Halley's Comet champagne, 1986 vintage, in my garden in Selsey.*

24

And finally... not *The Sky at Night!*

◄ (previous page) *Walking along the Prime Meridian during the Greenwich celebrations — it was sheer chance that the line happened the pass through a lake!*

When I first faced a television camera I had not the remotest idea that I would ever be called upon to take part in programmes other than astronomical ones. Yet as the years passed by I found myself drawn into all sorts of things. Not all of them were scientific; in particular I have often been on the panel of *Any Questions?* in which I am widely regarded as a menace because of my habit of saying precisely what I believe. I have also been involved in various appeals for handicapped children and hospital patients, and I only hope that I have managed to be of some use. On a more light-hearted note, there had been music.

As a musician I am a complete fake. I have never had a lesson in my life, but I taught myself to read and write musically when I was about eight, and, through no merit of my own, I know that I have that elusive thing called perfect pitch.[1] I play the xylophone, and have done so a good many times on television, even during the Royal Command Performance at Drury Lane in 1983. On one occasion, too, I joined in an orchestral concert in the Albert Hall. It was the Gerard Hoffnung Memorial Concert, and I was the third ocarina in the Surprise Symphony, conducted by Donald Swann. I can assure you that there were plenty of surprises.

What else? Well, during one televised Lenny and Jerry show, Lenny announced that the cameras were going over to a couple of East End comedians who weren't doing too badly. The comedians were Magnus Pyke and myself; we were the Hit Parade of 1881.

A slightly more astronomically related programme was my *One Pair of Eyes* in 1969, when I interviewed people who are sometimes classed as cranks but by me, more charitably, as Independent Thinkers. Pre-eminent among them is the Rev. P.H. Francis, former Vicar of Stoughton in Sussex, who has an excellent mathematics degree from Cambridge University, and who is firmly convinced that the Sun is cold. To him what we call the Sun is merely the gravitational centre of the Solar System, and is probably not solid. As he points out, heat cannot travel through a vacuum (otherwise the familiar Thermos flask would not work), and there are millions of miles of vacuum between us and the Sun. During our broadcast he gave his opinion that 'the notion of an incandescent Sun is childish, and not worthy of a grown-up person'. He amplified this by citing the case of an electric generating station. When you switch on your drawing-

---

[1] *On the debit side, I am absolutely devoid of artistic ability. In November 1986 I was called upon to 'doodle a duck' on a television programme devoted to the National Society for the Protection of Birds, and I am told that my effort looked, if anything, like a demented dinosaur.*

room fire the bars get hot, but the generator which provides the power is not hot, and the same principle applies to the Sun. Stars have no real existence, and are merely reflections of the Sun off the curved surface of infinity. It is absurd to talk about distances greater than infinity; however, sunlight can pass through it and reappear on the opposite side, suitably weakened, so that very faint stars are the images of the back of the Sun.

To film this interview we went to Stoughton Vicarage, which is near Chichester in a particularly beautiful part of Sussex. It was winter; we wanted a cosy scene, and Mr Francis suggested that we might liven up the drawing-room fire by pouring a little paraffin on to it. Unfortunately, we were rather over-generous, and while the cameras were running we became conscious of a dull roaring, followed by clouds of black smoke billowing from the hearth. I am glad to say that the local fire brigade dealt with the situation very promptly, and there was no harm done. Mr Francis himself — a delightful person — was not in the least put out, and said that it had indeed been a most interesting afternoon.

Another of our interviewees was Mr John Bradbury of Ashton-under-Lyne, whose scientific views are the reverse of orthodox. The Earth is flat, and is surrounded by the solid background of the universe, while the Moon is a small body made of 'plasticine phosphorus', showing at times two finger-like projections. Mr Bradbury has gone so far as to build a telescope which can show the background of the cosmos, though admittedly it will not reveal anything that a normal telescope will do. His method is to use at least a dozen lenses,

▲ *John Bradbury, in 1969, showing me his drawing of a finger-like projection from the Moon which he had observed with his unique telescope. (Only one projection was to be seen, as I established.)*

▼ *The late Samuel Shenton, presiding genius of the Flat Earth Society, showing me his idea of the shape of the world in a programme televised in 1969.*

placed one in front of the other, on the very reasonable assumption that when working together they will collect more light than any single lens can do. When he poked the telescope out of his bedroom window to demonstrate the way to align it the camera crew and other members of our team were suitable impressed. Momentarily I cast my mind back to Francis Jackson's Martian cactus.

I was also struck by Mr Bradbury's definition of 'light'. It is, he said, nothing more than 'darkness, lit up'.

Then there was the Aetherius Society, whose members are in constant touch with higher beings on Venus, Mars and elsewhere. Aetherius himself is a Venusian, and looks after the Earth, communicating by the telepathic powers of the Society's President and founder, the Rev. Dr Sir George King, formerly a London taxi-driver and now resident in California. Members organize regular Spiritual Pushes, and publish a magazine, *Cosmic Voice*, in which all Solar System activities are reported. Mr (I am sorry; the Rev. Dr Sir George) King was initially wary of me, as he harboured unworthy suspicions that I might be associated with some curiously named contributors to *Cosmic Voice* such as Walter Wümpe, N. Ormuss, R. Hugh Hall-Wright and Egon Spünraas, but when we went to the Society's headquarters in the Fulham Road we were cordially greeted, and were able to interview the official representative, Mr Robertson.

Apparently we had arrived at an opportune moment, because we had unknowingly been under attack from fish-men from the other side of the Galaxy. A missile had been launched towards us, but luckily the news had filtered through to the Interplanetary Parliament, which meets on Saturn, the most advanced of the planets, so that the missile was located and then destroyed by a thunderbolt launched from Mars. I asked Mr Robertson what the Saturnians looked like. 'You would see them in their entirety,' he replied, 'and they would appear as large ovoids, thirty or forty feet in diameter.' I commented that they sounded like balls, and Mr Robertson agreed that 'they are, in fact, complete balls,' with which description I could not possibly argue.

We talked to the astrologers, the UFO enthusiasts, the flat-earthers and the hollow-globers; we interviewed Mr Bernard Byron, who can speak the language of Venus fluently; and my only failure was to involve Mme Gabrielle Henriet, who is French by birth but who lives in Storrington. She believes the sky to be solid, and points out that the seasons cannot possibly be due to the changing tilt of the Earth's axis, because in such a case very tall buildings such as the Eiffel Tower would sway gently to and fro — which they demonstrably don't. Mme

Henriet said that she would have liked to have joined me, but dared not do so, because she was sure that as soon as she faced a television camera her false teeth would fall out.

My only other regret was that we could not find room for a Mr McGregor, of Glasgow, who spends all his time in collecting the registration numbers of bassoons. I know him to be a genuine scholar, because when I once sent him a number he told me that it was only a piccolo, in which he was perfectly correct. After some discussion, we decided that he did not really fit into the programme.

Over the years I have also conducted some peculiar radio interviews. On the *Today* programme, then master-minded by Jack de Manio, I talked to the President of the Fairy Research Society, who ended with a touching little message: if you are gardening, and must kill slugs, do it kindly, and without bitterness in your heart. We also made a dead-of-night expedition to a blasted heath near Watford, to talk to a coven of white witches. When we came back and played the tapes we fell in heaps on the floor, but we couldn't possibly broadcast them; all we really salvaged was the mewing of the cat.

▲ (Above left) Practising my leg-breaks in the cricket nets — the end of my long, kangaroo-leap run. At least I spin the ball hard, even if my length would not appeal to the Test selectors. (Above right) Batting practice. I have taken many more wickets than I have made runs; my average last season was 0.61, with a top score of 2 (actually the result of a dropped catch in the slips).

I have often been 'taken off' by impersonators. I have already mentioned the way in which the Two Ronnies destroyed our orrery opening. I have been one of Mike Yarwood's regular victims, and I did once make a mild protest. Over my left eyebrow I have a pronounced scar, which I always claim was due to injury in a wartime bombing raid, when we were caught in a sea of flak, had German fighters firing down at us, and were in the jaws of death. (Actually I came off my motor-cycle in 1952, when my front wheel caught in a rut, but the other story sounds better.) Mike got the scar wrong, but after I pointed this out he kindly repositioned it.

I always feel that people tend to take themselves much too seriously, but at least I don't think that can be held against me, so let me end this rather irrelevant chapter with two episodes dating from the Apollo period. During one of the missions, a viewer rang me up in the studio. 'Last night, on BBC2 Late Night Line-up, there was a most wicked and unkind impression of you by someone who looked a little like you, dressed in a space-suit and a fishbowl helmet, claiming to be a Martian who had come down to prove that there can't be any intelligent life on Earth because of the thick air and the tremendous amount of water. Do you know who it was?' I did — I thought I had disguised myself just sufficiently.

At about the same period I rode the Emmet Lunacycle, a remarkable contraption equipped with such refinements as a cheese comparator (to test the quality of the Moon's surface), an astrocat (to make sure you land the right way up) and a meteorite umbrella. I gave a deadpan commentary, and was later phoned by a reporter on the London *Evening Standard* who wanted to clear up one vital point: had that bicycle really been taken to the Moon?

* * * * * * * *

And with those recollections I think I have said enough. My thirty years with *The Sky at Night* have been great fun, and I hope for many more in the future, because I will certainly carry on as long as the BBC wants me to broadcast and people are willing to listen. On a more serious note, it does give me immense pleasure to come across well-known astronomers, both professional and amateur, who have been started on their careers by watching a programme I have presented or reading a book I have written. My role in astronomy, if I have one, is in urging others to do things which I could never do myself, because I haven't the skill. Whether I succeed or not must be left to others to judge, but at least I can say, in all sincerity, that I have done my best.

▼ *Riding the Emmet Lunacycle, the remarkable piece of mechanism which was not actually taken to the moon!*

Index

References to illustrations are italicized.

Acknowledgments

The author and publishers wish to thank the British Broadcasting
Corporation, London, and the National Aeronautics and Space
Administration, California, for permission to reproduce photographs in
this book. In addition, they would also like to thank the following:

Daily Telegraph Colour Library: illustrations on pages 81, 175 and
between pages 64-5 and 120-1 (photograph of Stonehenge
by M. Goddard)
Fox Photos: illustration on pages 114-15
Mark Gerson: illustration on page 7
Mary Evans Picture Library: illustrations between pages
    56-7 and 126-7
Jack Neilson: illustration facing page 144
The Photo Source: illustrations between pages 134-5 and
    152-3
Science Photo Library: illustration between pages 140-1
    (photo John Sanford)

Index

*References to illustrations
are italicized.*

Acknowledgments

The author and publishers wish to thank the British Broadcasting
Corporation, London, and the National Aeronautics and Space
Administration, California, for permission to reproduce photographs in
this book. In addition, they would also like to thank the following:

Daily Telegraph Colour Library: illustrations on pages 81, 175 and
between pages 64-5 and 120-1 (photograph of Stonehenge
by M. Goddard)
Fox Photos: illustration on pages 114-15
Mark Gerson: illustration on page 7
Mary Evans Picture Library: illustrations between pages
    56-7 and 126-7
Jack Neilson: illustration facing page 144
The Photo Source: illustrations between pages 134-5 and
    152-3
Science Photo Library: illustration between pages 140-1
    (photo John Sanford)